SOLUTIONS

COARSE SUSPENSION **COLLIODAL DISPERSION** **TRUE SOLUTION** **STRAINED PLUMS**

TASK CARD SERIES

Conceived and written by
Ron Marson
Illustrated by
Peg Marson

TOPS LEARNING SYSTEMS

10970 S. Mulino Rd.
Canby OR 97013

Oh, those pesky COPYRIGHT RESTRICTIONS!

Dear Educator,

TOPS is a nonprofit organization dedicated to educational ideals, not our bottom line. We have invested much time, energy, money, and love to bring you this excellent teaching resource.

And we have carefully designed this book to run on simple materials you already have or can easily purchase. If you consider the depth and quality of this curriculum amortized over years of teaching, it is dirt cheap, orders of magnitude less than prepackaged kits and textbooks.

Please honor our copyright restrictions. We are a very small company, and book sales are our life blood. When you buy this book and use it for your own teaching, you sustain our publishing effort. If you give or "loan" this book or copies of our lessons to other teachers, with no compensation to TOPS, you squeeze us financially, and may drive us out of business. Our well-being rests in your hands.

What if you are excited about the terrific ideas in this book, and want to share them with your colleagues? What if the teacher down the hall, or your homeschooling neighbor, is begging you for good science, quick! We have suggestions. Please see our *Purchase and Royalty Options* below.

We are grateful for the work you are doing to help shape tomorrow. We are honored that you are making TOPS a part of your teaching effort. Thank you for your good will and kind support.

Sincerely, Ron Marson

Purchase and Royalty Options:

Individual teachers, homeschoolers, libraries:

PURCHASE option: If your colleagues ask to borrow your book, please ask them to read this copyright page, and to contact TOPS for our current catalog so they can purchase their own book. We also have an **online catalog** that you can access at www.topscience.org.

If you are reselling a **used book** to another classroom teacher or homeschooler, please be aware that this still affects us by eliminating a potential book sale. We do not push "newer and better" editions to encourage consumerism. So we ask seller or purchaser (or both!) to acknowledge the ongoing value of this book by sending a contribution to support our continued work. Let your conscience be your guide.

Honor System ROYALTIES: If you wish to make copies from a library, or pass on copies of just a few activities in this book, please calculate their value at 50 cents (25 cents for homeschoolers) per lesson per recipient. Send that amount, or ask the recipient to send that amount, to TOPS. We also gladly accept donations. We know life is busy, but please do follow through on your good intentions promptly. It will only take a few minutes, and you'll know you did the right thing!

Schools and Districts:

You may wish to use this curriculum in several classrooms, in one or more schools. Please observe the following:

PURCHASE option: Order this book in quantities equal to the number of target classrooms. If you order 5 books, for example, then you have unrestricted use of this curriculum in any 5 classrooms per year for the life of your institution. You may order at these quantity discounts:

2-9 copies: 90% of current catalog price + shipping.

10+ copies: 80% of current catalog price + shipping.

ROYALTY option: Purchase 1 book *plus* photocopy or printing rights in quantities equal to the number of designated classrooms. If you pay for 5 Class Licenses, for example, then you have purchased reproduction rights for any 5 classrooms per year for the life of your institution.

1-9 Class Licenses: 70% of current book price per classroom.

10+ Class Licenses: 60% of current book price per classroom.

Workshops and Training Programs:

We are grateful to all of you who spread the word about TOPS. Please limit duplication to only those lessons you will be using, and collect all copies afterward. No take-home copies, please. Copies of copies are prohibited. Ask us for a free shipment of as many current **TOPS Ideas** catalogs as you need to support your efforts. Every catalog contains numerous free sample teaching ideas.

CONTENTS

PART I — INTRODUCTION

A. A TOPS Model for Effective Science Teaching
C. Getting Ready
D. Gathering Materials
E. Sequencing Task Cards
F. Long Range Objectives
G. Review / Test Questions

PART II — TEACHING NOTES

PART III — REPRODUCIBLE STUDENT TASK CARDS

A TOPS Model for Effective Science Teaching...

If science were only a set of explanations and a collection of facts, you could teach it with blackboard and chalk. You could assign students to read chapters and answer the questions that followed. Good students would take notes, read the text, turn in assignments, then give you all this information back again on a final exam. Science is traditionally taught in this manner. Everybody learns the same body of information at the same time. Class togetherness is preserved.

But science is more than this.

Science is also process — a dynamic interaction of rational inquiry and creative play. Scientists probe, poke, handle, observe, question, think up theories, test ideas, jump to conclusions, make mistakes, revise, synthesize, communicate, disagree and discover. Students can understand science as process only if they are free to think and act like scientists, in a classroom that recognizes and honors individual differences.

Science is *both* a traditional body of knowledge *and* an individualized process of creative inquiry. Science as process cannot ignore tradition. We stand on the shoulders of those who have gone before. If each generation reinvents the wheel, there is no time to discover the stars. Nor can traditional science continue to evolve and redefine itself without process. Science without this cutting edge of discovery is a static, dead thing.

Here is a teaching model that combines the best of both elements into one integrated whole. It is only a model. Like any scientific theory, it must give way over time to new and better ideas. We challenge you to incorporate this TOPS model into your own teaching practice. Change it and make it better so it works for you.

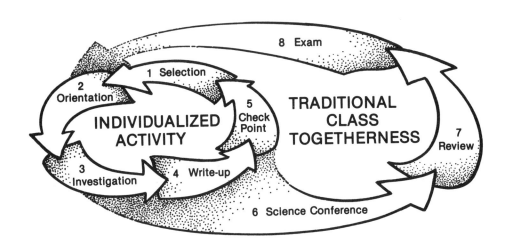

1. SELECTION

Doing TOPS is as easy as selecting the first task card and doing what it says, then the second, then the third, and so on. Working at their own pace, students fall into a natural routine that creates stability and order. They still have questions and problems, to be sure, but students know where they are and where they need to go.

Students generally select task cards in sequence because new concepts build on old ones in a specific order. There are, however, exceptions to this rule: students might *skip* a task that is not challenging; *repeat* a task with doubtful results; *add* a task of their own design to answer original "what would happen if" questions.

2. ORIENTATION

Many students will simply read a task card and immediately understand what to do. Others will require further verbal interpretation. Identify poor readers in your class. When they ask, "What does this mean?" they may be asking in reality, "Will you please read this card aloud?"

With such a diverse range of talent among students, how can you individualize activity and still hope to finish this module as a cohesive group? It's easy. By the time your most advanced students have completed all the task cards, including the enrichment series at the end, your slower students have at least completed the basic core curriculum. This core provides the common background so necessary for meaningful discussion, review and testing on a class basis.

3. INVESTIGATION

Students work through the task cards independently and cooperatively. They follow their own experimental strategies and help each other. You encourage this behavior by helping students only *after* they have tried to help themselves. As a resource person, you work to stay *out* of the center of attention, answering student questions rather than posing teacher questions.

When you need to speak to everyone at once, it is appropriate to interrupt individual task card activity and address the whole class, rather than repeat yourself over and over again. If you plan ahead, you'll find that most interruptions can fit into brief introductory remarks at the beginning of each new period.

4. WRITE-UP

Task cards ask students to explain the "how and why" of things. Write-ups are brief and to the point. Students may accelerate their pace through the task cards by writing these reports out of class.

Students may work alone or in cooperative lab groups. But each one must prepare an original write-up. These must be brought to the teacher for approval as soon as they are completed. Avoid dealing with too many write-ups near the end of the module, by enforcing this simple rule: each write-up must be approved *before* continuing on to the next task card.

5. CHECK POINT

The student and teacher evaluate each write-up together on a pass/no-pass basis. (Thus no time is wasted haggling over grades.) If the student has made reasonable effort consistent with individual ability, the write-up is checked off on a progress chart and included in the student's personal assignment folder or notebook kept on file in class.

Because the student is present when you evaluate, feedback is immediate and effective. A few seconds of this direct student-teacher interaction is surely more effective than 5 minutes worth of margin notes that students may or may not heed. Remember, you don't have to point out every error. Zero in on particulars. If reasonable effort has not been made, direct students to make specific improvements, and see you again for a follow-up check point.

A responsible lab assistant can double the amount of individual attention each student receives. If he or she is mature and respected by your students, have the assistant check the even-numbered write-ups while you check the odd ones. This will balance the work load and insure that all students receive equal treatment.

6. SCIENCE CONFERENCE

After individualized task card activity has ended, this is a time for students to come together, to discuss experimental results, to debate and draw conclusions. Slower students learn about the enrichment activities of faster students. Those who did original investigations, or made unusual discoveries, share this information with their peers, just like scientists at a real conference. This conference is open to films, newspaper articles and community speakers. It is a perfect time to consider the technological and social implications of the topic you are studying.

7. READ AND REVIEW

Does your school have an adopted science textbook? Do parts of your science syllabus still need to be covered? Now is the time to integrate other traditional science resources into your overall program. Your students already share a common background of hands-on lab work. With this shared base of experience, they can now read the text with greater understanding, think and problem-solve more successfully, communicate more effectively.

You might spend just a day on this step or an entire week. Finish with a review of key concepts in preparation for the final exam. Test questions in this module provide an excellent basis for discussion and study.

8. EXAM

Use any combination of the review/test questions, plus questions of your own, to determine how well students have mastered the concepts they've been learning. Those who finish your exam early might begin work on the first activity in the next new TOPS module.

Now that your class has completed a major TOPS learning cycle, it's time to start fresh with a brand new topic. Those who messed up and got behind don't need to stay there. Everyone begins the new topic on an equal footing. This frequent change of pace encourages your students to work hard, to enjoy what they learn, and thereby grow in scientific literacy.

GETTING READY

Here is a checklist of things to think about and preparations to make before your first lesson.

☐ Decide if this TOPS module is the best one to teach next.

TOPS modules are flexible. They can generally be scheduled in any order to meet your own class needs. Some lessons within certain modules, however, do require basic math skills or a knowledge of fundamental laboratory techniques. Review the task cards in this module now if you are not yet familiar with them. Decide whether you should teach any of these other TOPS modules first: *Measuring Length, Graphing, Metric Measure, Weighing* or *Electricity* (before *Magnetism*). It may be that your students already possess these requisite skills or that you can compensate with extra class discussion or special assistance.

☐ Number your task card masters in pencil.

The small number printed in the lower right corner of each task card shows its position within the overall series. If this ordering fits your schedule, copy each number into the blank parentheses directly above it at the top of the card. Be sure to use pencil rather than ink. You may decide to revise, upgrade or rearrange these task cards next time you teach this module. To do this, write your own better ideas on blank 4 x 6 index cards, and renumber them into the task card sequence wherever they fit best. In this manner, your curriculum will adapt and grow as you do.

☐ Copy your task card masters.

You have our permission to reproduce these task cards, for as long as you teach, with only 1 restriction: please limit the distribution of copies you make to the students you personally teach. Encourage other teachers who want to use this module to purchase their *own* copy. This supports TOPS financially, enabling us to continue publishing new TOPS modules for you. For a full list of task card options, please turn to the first task card masters numbered "cards 1-2."

☐ Collect needed materials.

Please see the opposite page.

☐ Organize a way to track completed assignment.

Keep write-ups on file in class. If you lack a vertical file, a box with a brick will serve. File folders or notebooks both make suitable assignment organizers. Students will feel a sense of accomplishment as they see their file folders grow heavy, or their notebooks fill up, with completed assignments. Easy reference and convenient review are assured, since all papers remain in one place.

Ask students to staple a sheet of numbered graph paper to the inside front cover of their file folder or notebook. Use this paper to track each student's progress through the module. Simply initial the corresponding task card number as students turn in each assignment.

☐ Review safety procedures.

Most TOPS experiments are safe even for small children. Certain lessons, however, require heat from a candle flame or Bunsen burner. Others require students to handle sharp objects like scissors, straight pins and razor blades. These task cards should not be attempted by immature students unless they are closely supervised. You might choose instead to turn these experiments into teacher demonstrations.

Unusual hazards are noted in the teaching notes and task cards where appropriate. But the curriculum cannot anticipate irresponsible behavior or negligence. It is ultimately the teacher's responsibility to see that common sense safety rules are followed at all times. Begin with these basic safety rules:

1. Eye Protection: Wear safety goggles when heating liquids or solids to high temperatures.
2. Poisons: Never taste anything unless told to do so.
3. Fire: Keep loose hair or clothing away from flames. Point test tubes which are heating away from your face and your neighbor's.
4. Glass Tubing: Don't force through stoppers. (The teacher should fit glass tubes to stoppers in advance, using a lubricant.)
5. Gas: Light the match first, before turning on the gas.

☐ Communicate your grading expectations.

Whatever your philosophy of grading, your students need to understand the standards you expect and how they will be assessed. Here is a grading scheme that counts individual effort, attitude and overall achievement. We think these 3 components deserve equal weight:

1. Pace (effort): Tally the number of check points you have initialed on the graph paper attached to each student's file folder or science notebook. Low ability students should be able to keep pace with gifted students, since write-ups are evaluated relative to individual performance standards. Students with absences or those who tend to work at a slow pace may (or may not) choose to overcome this disadvantage by assigning themselves more homework out of class.

2. Participation (attitude): This is a subjective grade assigned to reflect each student's attitude and class behavior. Active participators who work to capacity receive high marks. Inactive onlookers, who waste time in class and copy the results of others, receive low marks.

3. Exam (achievement): Task cards point toward generalizations that provide a base for hypothesizing and predicting. A final test over the entire module determines whether students understand relevant theory and can apply it in a predictive way.

Gathering Materials

Listed below is everything you'll need to teach this module. You already have many of these items. The rest are available from your supermarket, drugstore and hardware store. Laboratory supplies may be ordered through a science supply catalog. Hobby stores also carry basic science equipment.

Keep this classification key in mind as you review what's needed:

special in-a-box materials:	general on-the-shelf materials:
Italic type suggests that these materials are unusual. Keep these specialty items in a separate box. After you finish teaching this module, label the box for storage and put it away, ready to use again the next time you teach this module.	Normal type suggests that these materials are common. Keep these basics on shelves or in drawers that are readily accessible to your students. The next TOPS module you teach will likely utilize many of these same materials.
(substituted materials):	***optional materials:**
A parentheses following any item suggests a ready substitute. These alternatives may work just as well as the original, perhaps better. Don't be afraid to improvise, to make do with what you have.	An asterisk sets these items apart. They are nice to have, but you can easily live without them. They are probably not worth the extra trip, unless you are gathering other materials as well.

Everything is listed in order of first use. Start gathering at the top of this list and work down. Ask students to bring recycled items from home. The teaching notes may occasionally suggest additional student activity under the heading "Extensions." Materials for these optional experiments are listed neither here nor in the teaching notes. Read the extension itself to find out what new materials, if any, are required.

Needed quantities depend on how many students you have, how you organize them into activity groups, and how you teach. Decide which of these 3 estimates best applies to you, then adjust quantities up or down as necessary:

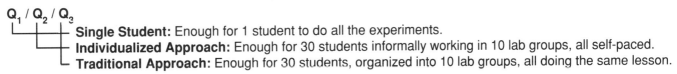

Q_1 / Q_2 / Q_3

Single Student: Enough for 1 student to do all the experiments.
Individualized Approach: Enough for 30 students informally working in 10 lab groups, all self-paced.
Traditional Approach: Enough for 30 students, organized into 10 lab groups, all doing the same lesson.

KEY: *special in-a-box materials* *(substituted materials)*	general on-the-shelf materials *optional materials

1/1/1	roll commercial-grade, soft paper towels	1/1/1	package rice
1/10/10	scissors	1/1/1	*envelope of powdered milk*
1/1/1	roll school-grade "hard" paper towels (laboratory-quality filters)	1/1/1	*small container flour, bleached or unbleached*
		1/5/10	rolls clear tape
1/1/1	packages: corn starch, granulated sugar, *alum*, fine-grained table salt, baking soda, *copper sulfate*, *rock salt*, *Epsom salt*; include a dispensing spoon with each package	1/10/10	graduated cylinders, 10 mL capacity
		1/1/1	box seltzer tablets, Alka-Seltzer or equivalent
		1/1/1	box sugar cubes
		1/6/10	microscope slides
3/30/30	baby food jars, most with lids (small beakers)	1/1/1	box facial tissues (roll toilet paper)
1/1/1	water source; use distilled water if source is hard	1/4/10	*microscopes
1/6/10	dropper bottles: *iodine*, rubbing alcohol	1/1/1	package rubber bands
1/3/6	dropper bottles: *chlorine bleach*, mineral oil, liquid detergent, *India ink*, vinegar, *distilled water*	1/1/1	*can scouring cleanser*
		1/10/10	index cards
		1/2/4	paper punches
1/1/1	hot plate with teapot (Bunsen burner or alcohol lamps and matches)	1/1/1	box plastic straws
		1/1/1	wall clock with second hand (stop watch)
2/10/20	eyedroppers	1/6/10	mass balances — instruments constructed in TOPS module, *Weighing 05,* are suitable
1/1/2	*packets non-dairy creamer*		
1 /1/1	*shaker of pepper*	1/10/10	*calculators
3/30/30	test tubes, 12 mL capacity or more	1/5/10	small Pyrex beakers
1/5/10	magnifying glasses	1/6/10	clothespins
1/10/10	small paper drinking cups	1/4/10	permanent markers
1/4/10	*metric rulers	1/1/1	*bottle calcium acetate* — activity 27 only
1/1/1	roll aluminum foil	1/1/1	*bottle sodium thiosulfate* — activity 28 only

Sequencing Task Cards

This logic tree shows how all the task cards in this module tie together. In general, students begin at the trunk of the tree and work up through the related branches. As the diagram suggests, the way to upper level activities leads up from lower level activities.

At the teacher's discretion, certain activities can be omitted or sequences changed to meet specific class needs. The only activities that must be completed in sequence are indicated by leaves that open *vertically* into the ones above them. In these cases the lower activity is a prerequisite to the upper.

When possible, students should complete the task cards in the same sequence as numbered. If time is short, however, or certain students need to catch up, you can use the logic tree to identify concept-related *horizontal* activities. Some of these might be omitted since they serve only to reinforce learned concepts rather than introduce new ones.

On the other hand, if students complete all the activities at a certain horizontal concept level, then experience difficulty at the next higher level, you might go back down the logic tree to have students repeat specific key activities for greater reinforcement.

For whatever reason, when you wish to make sequence changes, you'll find this logic tree a valuable reference. Parentheses in the upper right corner of each task card allow you total flexibility. They are left blank so you can pencil in sequence numbers of your own choosing.

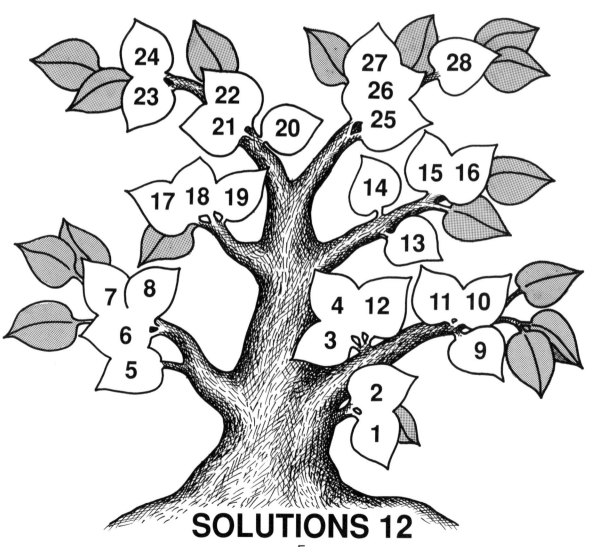

SOLUTIONS 12

E

LONG-RANGE OBJECTIVES

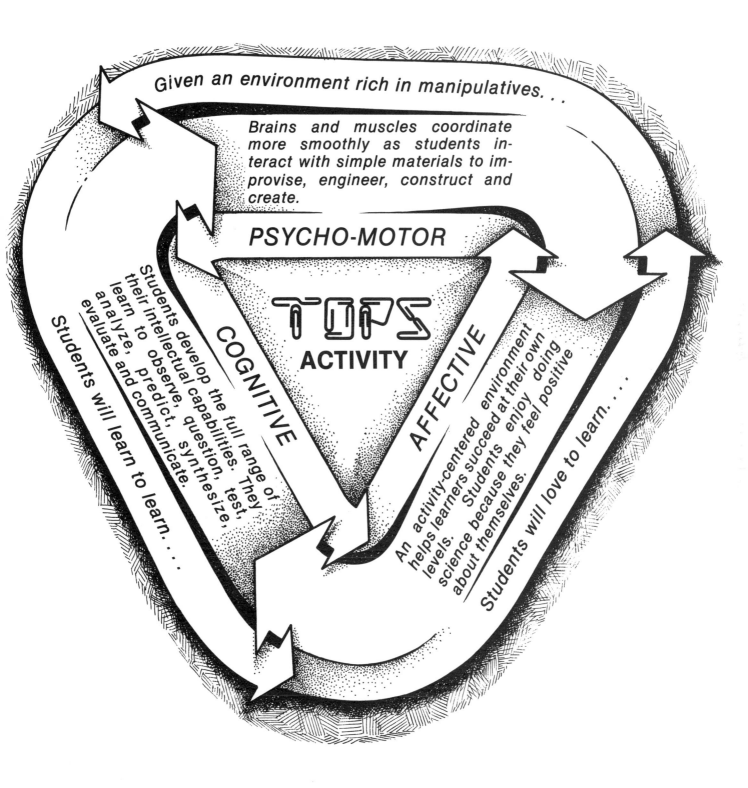

Given an environment rich in manipulatives...

Brains and muscles coordinate more smoothly as students interact with simple materials to improvise, engineer, construct and create.

PSYCHO-MOTOR

TOPS
ACTIVITY

COGNITIVE

Students develop the full range of their intellectual capabilities. They learn to observe, question, test, analyze, predict, synthesize, evaluate and communicate.

Students will learn to learn....

AFFECTIVE

An activity-centered environment helps learners succeed at their own levels. Students enjoy doing science because they feel positive about themselves.

Students will love to learn....

Review / Test Questions

Photocopy the questions below. On a separate sheet of blank paper, cut and paste those boxes you want to use as test questions. Include questions of your own design, as well. Crowd all these questions onto a single page for students to answer on another paper, or leave space for student responses after each question, as you wish. Duplicate a class set and your custom-made test is ready to use. Use leftover questions as a review in preparation for the final exam.

task 1
You filter a bucket of gravel through a wire screen that has squares measuring 2 cm on a side. Rocks that pass though are then filtered through a smaller screen with squares measuring 1 cm on a side. What size gravel is trapped in between? Explain.

task 2
a. Explain how a coffee filter separates fresh brewed coffee from the grounds.
b. Suppose you ran out of coffee filters. Describe another method, other than filtering, to separate the liquid from the grounds.

task 3
When clay is mixed in water the solution turns cloudy, but when sugar is mixed in water the solution remains clear. What does this tell you about the size of the particles in each solution?

task 2-3
How would you use a filter and iodine to prove that starch particles in water are reduced in size when heated to boiling?

task 4,12
Classify each mixture as a coarse suspension, colloidal dispersion or true solution. Give a reason for each answer.
a. Milk
b. Sea water.
c. A seasoning sauce that says "shake before using.

task 5
A mixture of sand, silt and clay is called loam. How would you determine if the soil in your area qualifies as loam?

task 6
Describe how you would clear each colloidal dispersion in water:
a. Clay.
b. India ink.
c. Milk.

task 7
Is the water in a swimming pool purified by adding chlorine tablets? Explain.

task 8
You are lost in the desert with only a shovel, a large clear plastic tarp and a bucket. You discover moisture in the soil at a depth of 1 meter, but no liquid water. Design a solar still to help you survive.

task 5, 8
A pinch of sand, clay and salt are mixed in a glass of water. How would you…
a. remove only the sand?
b. remove both the sand and clay?
c. remove all impurities at once?

task 9
Soap film is extremely thin and transparent. Nevertheless, a soap bubble is easy to see as it floats through the air. How can this be?

task 9
Detergents are often used to clean up oil tanker spills at sea. Do these detergent really "clean" the water?

task 10-11
A lump of sugar is dropped into a clear glass of water.
a. Account for the wavy turbulence surrounding the dissolving cube.
b. Why does the lump eventually disappear?

task 10-11
Corn oil, alcohol and water are combined in graduates with these results:
10.0 mL corn oil + 10.0 mL water = 20.0 mL mixture
10.0 mL alcohol + 10.0 mL water = 19.8 mL solution
Account for the difference in volume.

task 4,12
Identify each of the following as a coarse suspension, colloidal dispersion or true solution:
a. _____ The cloudy solution will not settle.
b. _____ The solute dissolves in the solvent.
c. _____ The cloudy solution clears when filtered, but you must first add a coagulant.
d. _____ The cloudy solution clears if allowed to settle.
e. _____ The clear, colorless solution leaves a residue behind as it evaporates.
f. _____ The cloudy solution clears when filtered.

task 13
A teaspoon of blue, grape-flavored powder is added to a glass of water. It is then stirred until the powder completely dissolves. Explain when the solution is homogeneous and when it is heterogeneous.

task 13-14
You can increase the rate that a solute dissolves in a solvent by stirring the solution. Name 2 additional ways to increase this dissolving rate.

Answers

task 1
Rocks captured in between the screens measure between 1 cm and 2 cm in diameter. Rocks larger than 2 cm were trapped by the first filter. Rocks smaller than 1 cm passed through both filters.

task 2
a. The coffee grounds are larger than the pores in the filter paper. They are trapped by the filter while the liquid coffee passes through.
b. Wait a little while, allowing gravity to settle the coffee grounds to the bottom of the pot. Then gently pour off the clear liquid into a clean cup.

task 3
The particles of clay in solution are large enough to absorb and scatter light, causing the water to look cloudy. Sugar molecules, by contrast, don't interfere with the passage of light, so they must be much smaller than the clay particles.

task 2-3
First filter an unboiled starch solution. The filtrate will not give a positive starch test with iodine because the starch particles are too large to pass through the filter. Then heat a starch solution to boiling and filter it. This time the filtrate will turn blue-black with iodine. Some of the starch particles dissolved into the water as much smaller molecules, and passed through the pores of the filter paper.

task 4,12
a. Milk is a colloidal dispersion. It remains opaque and won't settle.
b. Sea water is a true solution. Its dissolved minerals (ions) are too small to absorb or scatter light, so the solution looks clear.
c. The sauce is a coarse suspension. The undissolved seasonings must be remixed before each use because they are coarse enough to settle over time.

task 5
Mix the soil sample in a jar of water and allow it to settle. It could be classified as loam if you could see all 3 components: sand near the bottom, silt above that, clay at the very top of the sediment with a suspension of finer clay particles in the water above.

task 6
a. Add alum or other aluminum salt to coagulate the clay, then clear by filtering or settling.
b. Add vinegar to the India ink, then clear by filtering or settling.
c. Sour the milk. (Add vinegar or lemon juice, or simply keep the milk in a warm place.) Solid white curds will form above a clear liquid whey.

task 7
Harmful bacteria are killed but nothing is removed. Toxins that were in the water before treatment will still be there.

task 8
Dig out a square pit deeper than 1 meter. Put the bucket at the center. Lay the clear plastic tarp over the top, weighing down the perimeter with rocks or dirt. Put one additional rock or clump of dirt in the center, so the tarp will slope down to a central point just above the bucket. Go rest in the shade (if you can find any) as your solar still condenses evaporated ground water on the underside of the plastic sheet and drips it into the bucket.

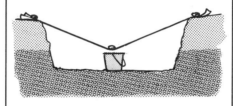

task 5, 8
a. Pour the glass of water through a filter or allow it to settle.
b. Coagulate the suspended particles with an aluminum salt, like alum. Then filter the solution or allow it to settle.
c. Distill the water, leaving all sand, clay and salt behind. Capture the pure distillate in another container.

task 9
Light is refracted and reflected as it passes through the surface film. It is this bending of light rays on the surface of the bubble that makes it visible.

task 9
No. They form an emulsion with the oil, breaking it up into tiny drops that disperse through the water. This breaks up the oil slick, but oil still remains in the water.

task 10-11
a. Light refracts as it passes through parts of the solution with different densities. This effect is most pronounced near the surface of the sugar cube where sugar concentrations are the greatest.
b. Individual molecules of sugar separate from the cube and mix between the water molecules. Once separated, these sugar molecules are much too small to block or scatter light on an individual basis. And so they disappear.

task 10-11
Corn oil rests directly on top of water without mixing. As expected, the sum of the parts (10.0 mL + 10.0 mL) equals the whole (20.0 mL). There is a slight but significant loss of .2 mL when alcohol and water are combined. As alcohol molecules dissolve between water molecules, they pack together a little more tightly, taking up less space as a solution than when they were unmixed.

task 4,12
a. colloidal dispersion
b. true solution
c. colloidal dispersion
d. coarse suspension
e. true solution
f. coarse suspension

task 13
The solution is homogeneous only after the powder completely dissolves, becoming equally distributed throughout the water as a uniform grape-blue solution. Before the solution is stirred, it remains heterogeneous, with the greatest concentration of grape blue at the bottom.

task 13-14
Heat the solvent to increase its temperature. Or crush the solute into smaller particles to increase its surface area.

Review / Test Questions (continued)

task 14
Which dissolves faster in water, a gram of granulated sugar or a gram of powdered sugar? Explain.

task 15
Describe how to prepare a saturated solution of copper sulfate in water.

task 15
Water from the Dead Sea has a much higher concentration of salt than ocean water. How would you experiment with Dead Sea water to determine if it was saturated or unsaturated?

task 16
Would you expect a seltzer table to dissolve faster in distilled water, sea water or saturated salt water? Justify your answer.

task 17
Do ice crystals form for the same reason that salt crystals form? Explain.

task 18
Crystals grow by repeating a unit pattern. Does this mean that all crystal formations of the same salt also have the same shape? Explain.

task 17-18
You find an unlabeled bottle of clear colorless salt solution in your laboratory. What could you do to identify this salt?

task 19
The president of Acme Water Systems asks you to do a television commercial to scientifically demonstrate that Acme distilled water is the purest form of water that you can buy. Design a commercial.

task 20
A crystal of rock salt is added to a test tube of fully saturated salt water, then sealed with a cork.
a. Will the salt crystal gradually disappear? Explain.
b. Will the salt crystal retain its original surface atoms? Explain.

task 21-22
It is determined by experiment that 20 grams of salt will dissolve in 100 mL of water when stirred moderately for 1 minute. Can you use this data to predict how many grams of salt will dissolve in the same amount of water if it is stirred moderately for 2 minutes?

task 21-22
Exactly 40 grams of a red salt is added to 100 grams of water. The water is stirred slowly and constantly while its increasing salt concentration is recorded every 5 minutes by a light-absorption device. Here are the results for the first half hour:

time (min)	concentration (g salt/100 g H_2O)
0	0
5	16
10	22
15	26
20	28
25	29
30	29

a. Make a graph of time vs. concentration.
b. What is the concentration of this salt solution at saturation?
c. How many grams of salt remain undissolved at the bottom of the beaker?

task 23
You are given two salt samples in test tubes. One is hydrated, the other is anhydrous. How can you tell which is which?

task 24
Exactly 20.0 grams of a certain salt is thoroughly heated and then reweighed. Its new mass is found to be 13.8 grams.
a. How much water of hydration was driven off?
b. Express this water of hydration as a percentage of the total mass.

task 25-26
Just 5.0 g of alum dissolves in 100 g of cold water at 10° C to form a saturated solution. But twice that amount dissolves if the water is warmed to 27° C. Describe the solubility of this salt…
a. in words.
b. in numbered units of concentration.

task 25-26
The solubility of salts X and Y change with temperature as shown.

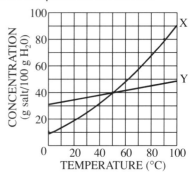

a. Qualitatively compare (in words) the solubility of each salt.
b. Quantitatively compare (in numbers) the solubility of each salt at room temperature (20° C).
c. Under what condition do both salts have equal solubilities? What is that solubility?

task 27
Air bubbles form on the inside of a pan as it is heated on the stove. Explain.

task 28
Your are given a supersaturated solution of sodium thiosulfate (hypo) in a test tube.
a. How would you recrystallize this solution?
b. Would you expect the temperature to change? Why?

Answers (continued)

task 14
A gram of powdered sugar dissolves faster than a gram of granulated sugar. Broken into many smaller particles, the powdered sugar has a greater portion of its molecules exposed at the surface, where they can make direct contact with water and dissolve.

task 15
Add copper sulfate to water and stir thoroughly until no more will dissolve.

task 15
Add just a small pinch of salt to a sample of Dead Sea water and stir vigorously. If this small trace will not dissolve, then the solution is saturated. If the pinch of salt does dissolve, then it is still unsaturated.

task 16
The seltzer table should dissolve fastest in distilled water. Since it is virtually pure, free of all dissolved salts, it has a higher proportion of intermolecular sites available to accept the dissolving seltzer table — more than either sea water or saturated water.

task 17
No. Ice crystals form because water freezes. Salt crystals form, usually at much higher temperatures, because water evaporates past its point of saturation, leaving behind dissolved salt that crystallizes out of solution.

task 18
No. The unit patterns grow to various sizes and assume diverse orientations, producing an infinite variety of final crystal formations.

task 17-18
Place a few drops of the solution on a microscope slide and allow it to evaporate to dryness. This will leave behind an array of crystals that you can perhaps identify by sight or compare with the crystals left behind by known salt solutions.

task 19
Evaporate a drop of Acme Water Systems distilled water next to equal-sized drops of water from Acme's competitors. Take a close-up photograph of the residue left behind for direct visual comparison.

task 20
a. No. The solution is fully saturated. It has no more capacity to dissolve additional salt.
b. No. The saturated solution is in dynamic equilibrium. Even though no more salt will dissolve, molecules will still crystallize onto the rock salt while an equal number dissolve back into solution. In time, the ions near the surface will be exchange with ions in solution.

task 21-22
No. When the salt is first mixed with water, it dissolves at its maximum rate. As the solution becomes more saturated, the salt dissolves progressively slower. If 20 g of salt dissolves over the first minute, certainly much less salt will dissolve over the second minute, but you can't predict how much.

task 21-22
a.

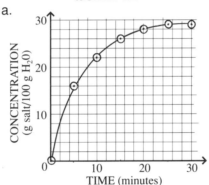

b. 29 g salt/100 g H_2O
c. 11 g undissolved salt remains

task 23
Gently heat both test tubes over a flame. The hydrated salt will likely sizzle and sputter, while its water of hydration condenses on the side of the test tube. The anhydrous salt should remain unchanged because there is no water of hydration to drive off.

task 24
a. Water of hydration =
   20.0 g - 13.8 g = 6.2 g.
b. $\dfrac{6.2 \text{ g}}{20.0 \text{ g}} \times 100 = 31\%$

task 25-26
a. Alum is moderately soluble in cold water but much more soluble in warm water.
b. solubility of alum at 10° C =
   5.0 g alum/100 g H_2O
   solubility of alum at 28° C =
   10.0 g alum/100 g H_2O

task 25-26
a. Salt X is less soluble in cold water than salt Y. With rising temperature the solubility of salt X increases more rapidly than the solubility of salt Y. In hot water salt X becomes more soluble than salt Y.
b. At room temperature (20° C), 20 g salt X/100 g H_2O dissolves, compared to 35 g salt Y/100 g H_2O.
c. At 50° C, both salts have equal solubilities of 40 g solute/100 g H_2O.

task 27
Dissolved air becomes less soluble in water with increasing temperatures. As it is forced out of solution, air bubbles form that cling to the side of the pan.

task 28
a. Drop a seed crystal of sodium thiosulfate into the supersaturated solution.
b. Yes. The test tube would warm up because the supersaturated form of hypo has higher energy than the more stable crystallized form.

TEACHING NOTES
For Activities 1-28

Task Objective (TO) compare the filtering capacity of soft and hard paper towels. To relate the porosity of filter paper to the size of particles in suspension.

TWO KINDS OF FILTERS ○ Solutions ( )

1. Fold a soft absorbent paper towel into quarters. Trim the 4 loose edges into a quarter circle to make a cone-shaped filter.

2. Make a second filter like the first, from a "hard," unbleached, school-grade paper towel.

FOLD AND TRIM   OPEN CONE

3. Mix a pinch of cornstarch in a small jar full of water. Filter part of this solution into 2 more jars, some through the soft filter and some through the hard filter.

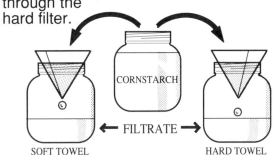

SOFT TOWEL   ← FILTRATE →   HARD TOWEL

4. Examine each *filtrate*. Are the cornstarch particles larger or smaller than the pores in each filter paper? Explain.

5. Add a drop of iodine to each filtrate. If cornstarch is present it will turn blue-black. What can you conclude?

6. Pour all 3 solutions into 1 jar. Close with a lid that is labeled with your name.

1

Answers / Notes

4. The filtrate under the *soft* paper towel is cloudy, indicating that the cornstarch particles were small enough to pass through its pores. The filtrate under the *hard* paper towel is clear, indicating that the cornstarch particles were larger than the pores in the filter paper and therefore trapped by the paper.

5. The cloudy filtrate (from the soft paper towel) turned a dingy grey, confirming the presence of starch. The clear filtrate (from the hard paper towel) was tinged yellow by the iodine, but indicated no starch.

6. *This coarse suspension of blue-black starch requires from 5 to 15 minutes to settle to the bottom of the jar, depending on the amount of starch added in the original pinch. Students may begin the next activity after it settles, or wait until tomorrow.*

Materials

☐ Soft, absorbent, paper towel. Any commercial brand name sold in grocery stores will do.

☐ Scissors.

☐ "Hard," unbleached, industrial-grade paper towel. Find this dispensed in rolls (not individual sheets) in the school lavatory. You may also substitute laboratory grade paper filters or coffee filters if the paper has a close weave that is dense enough to filter out cornstarch particles.

☐ Cornstarch from the grocery store. This and most dry goods used later may be conveniently dispensed directly from the box. Keep a spoon in the box so that students can easily manage the powder and "pinch" small amounts without waste or spilling.

☐ Three baby food jars with at least 1 lid. One additional lid will be needed later. These jars are widely used throughout this module. Small beakers may often be substituted, but lack the advantage of being sealable.

☐ A water source. This is a requirement in nearly all activities, but will only be mentioned in this first activity. If you don't have an adequate distribution of sinks and faucets, substitute water-filled bottles or pitchers, plus plastic tubs to contain the excess. If your water is exceptionally hard, substitute distilled water where appropriate.

☐ Iodine dispensed in a dropper bottle. Use tincture of iodine (sold in drug stores) full strength, or dilute with water for economy. You can make your own by adding 2 g iodine crystals and 5 g potassium iodide to a liter of water. Iodine is poisonous and stains clothing. It should carry an appropriate warning label.

☐ Masking tape.

(TO) clear a suspension by settling and by filtering. To understand how these processes work in nature.

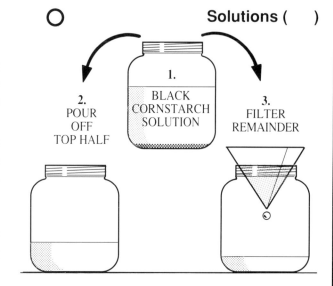

TWO WAYS TO PURIFY ○   Solutions (   )

1. Get your black cornstarch solution from the previous activity. Be careful not to unsettle the solution inside.

2. Gently pour off the clear top *half* into a second jar. How has gravity helped purify this solution?

3. Filter the remaining bottom half into a third jar. Will just any kind of filter paper work? What special property must it have?

4. Cornstarch forms a *coarse suspension* in cold water.
   a. Name 2 ways to purify a coarse suspension.
   b. Explain how these 2 ways happen similarly in nature to clear up the water we drink.

© 1990 by TOPS Learning Systems   2

Answers / Notes

2. Gravity pulled the corn-starch particles down to the bottom of the jar. This cleared the water above, allowing the top half to be separated into another jar.

3. To successfully filter the remaining water, the pores in the filter paper must be small enough to trap the corn starch particles. "Hard" school-grade paper towels have small enough pores; the pores in soft commercial-grade paper towels are too big.

   The kind of filter paper is not specified in this step. Most students will logically choose the school-grade variety because it worked best before. Students who decide to test the commercial variety as well will observe that the larger particles blacken the paper while the smaller particles pass through to darken the filtrate.

4a. (1) Allow the coarse suspension to settle, then pour off the clear liquid above it.
   (2) Pass the coarse suspension through a filter that has pores small enough to trap the suspended particles.

4b. (1) Muddy waters (from mountain glaciers, for example) enter calm lakes and reservoirs, where coarse sediment gradually settle to the bottom.
   (2) As muddy water sinks into the ground, it passes through layers of soil and sand that trap suspended particles, just like filter paper. When the water finally enters an underground stream or aquifer, it is clear.

Materials

☐ The black cornstarch and iodine solution saved from the previous activity.
☐ Two additional baby food jars.
☐ "Hard" school-grade paper towel.
☐ Soft commercial paper towel.
☐ Scissors.

(TO) relate the clarity of a solution to the size of particles it contains. To examine how saliva breaks down starch into simple sugars.

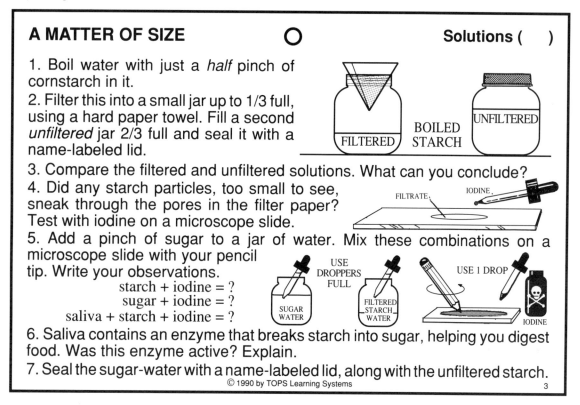

A MATTER OF SIZE   O   Solutions ( )

1. Boil water with just a *half* pinch of cornstarch in it.

2. Filter this into a small jar up to 1/3 full, using a hard paper towel. Fill a second *unfiltered* jar 2/3 full and seal it with a name-labeled lid.

3. Compare the filtered and unfiltered solutions. What can you conclude?

4. Did any starch particles, too small to see, sneak through the pores in the filter paper? Test with iodine on a microscope slide.

5. Add a pinch of sugar to a jar of water. Mix these combinations on a microscope slide with your pencil tip. Write your observations.

       starch + iodine = ?
       sugar + iodine = ?
saliva + starch + iodine = ?

6. Saliva contains an enzyme that breaks starch into sugar, helping you digest food. Was this enzyme active? Explain.

7. Seal the sugar-water with a name-labeled lid, along with the unfiltered starch.

© 1990 by TOPS Learning Systems   3

Introduction

Clean air is mostly a solution of nitrogen (N_2), oxygen (O_2) and water vapor (H_2O). As individual molecules, they are too small to block or scatter light. Thus the air looks perfectly clear.

• Water molecules condense (join together) to form tiny drops that grow and grow. Use this idea to explain why clouds and fog are difficult to see through. (The droplets grow large enough to block and scatter light.)

• Comment on the size of air pollution particles. (Air pollution particles are large enough to block or scatter light, making the air hazy and reducing visibility.)

Answers / Notes

3. The filtered solution is clear, while the unfiltered is slightly cloudy. The filter successfully removed starch from the solution. *(But not all, as your students will soon see!)*

4. The starch puddle tints blue-black with iodine. Even though some starch particles were trapped by the filter paper, other particles that were too small to see slipped through the filter. *(Starch comes in two forms. Insoluble long chained molecules are trapped by the filter paper; soluble shorter chained molecules pass on through.)*

5. *Colors are easiest to observe against white paper.*

     starch + iodine = positive (blue-black)
     sugar + iodine = negative (yellow)
     saliva + starch + iodine = negative (yellow)

6. Yes. Starch, in the presence of saliva is converted to sugar, resulting in a negative iodine test.

7. *Students may proceed directly to the next task card, though they will be more impressed to notice that some of the starch hasn't settled, even after 24 hours.*

Materials

☐ A dilute solution of starch that has been brought to a boil and allowed to cool. You can prepare this in advance by adding a teaspoon of starch to a pot of water and boiling over a stove or hot plate. Or if your lab is properly equipped, students can add a half pinch of starch to a Pyrex beaker and heat over a Bunsen burner. The directions in step 1 are not specific, leaving both options open. Tell students how you want them to proceed.

☐ Cornstarch.

☐ Three baby food jars and two lids.

☐ Refined granulated sugar. Dispense in its original packaging, keeping a spoon inside for easy retrieval.

☐ Masking tape and scissors.

☐ School-grade paper towel.

☐ A microscope slide and 2 eyedroppers.

☐ Iodine dispensed in a dropper bottle.

(TO) compare and contrast a coarse suspension, colloidal dispersion and true solution. To define and use basic vocabulary.

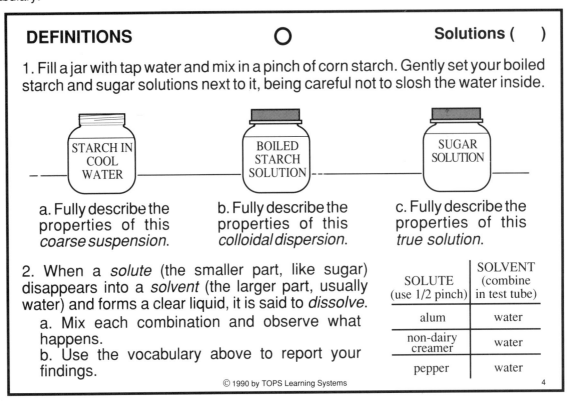

DEFINITIONS ○ Solutions ( )

1. Fill a jar with tap water and mix in a pinch of corn starch. Gently set your boiled starch and sugar solutions next to it, being careful not to slosh the water inside.

STARCH IN COOL WATER   BOILED STARCH SOLUTION   SUGAR SOLUTION

a. Fully describe the properties of this *coarse suspension*.

b. Fully describe the properties of this *colloidal dispersion*.

c. Fully describe the properties of this *true solution*.

2. When a *solute* (the smaller part, like sugar) disappears into a *solvent* (the larger part, usually water) and forms a clear liquid, it is said to *dissolve*.
   a. Mix each combination and observe what happens.
   b. Use the vocabulary above to report your findings.

SOLUTE (use 1/2 pinch)	SOLVENT (combine in test tube)
alum	water
non-dairy creamer	water
pepper	water

© 1990 by TOPS Learning Systems   4

Answers / Notes

1a. The coarse suspension in water was originally cloudy but cleared as it settled. The particles are large enough to be trapped by filter paper.

1b. The colloidal dispersion remains cloudy because its particles are too small to fully settle out. *(This jar may also contain some bottom residue that was course enough to settle.)*

The insoluble long-chained starch molecules that remain suspended in this colloidal dispersion can be cleared by filtration, as students learned in activity 3, step 4. Starch is exceptional in this respect. Most colloidal dispersions, such as clay in water, can't be cleared by filtration.

1c.   A true solution contains particles that are too small to scatter or block light. Thus it remains perfectly clear.

2b. • Alum dissolves into the water but the solvent remains clear. The solute and solvent have formed a true solution.
   • Nondairy creamer doesn't dissolve in water, since the solvent remains cloudy. It forms a colloidal dispersion that remains suspended without settling.
   • Pepper doesn't dissolve in water. It forms a coarse suspension that floats and settles in the solution.

Materials

☐ A baby food jar.
☐ Corn starch.
☐ The boiled-starch and sugar solutions from the previous activity.
☐ Alum. This is sold in drug stores as a traditional home chemical.
☐ Non-dairy creamer.
☐ Pepper.
☐ A test tube.

(TO) clear a mixture of soil and water by settling and filtration. To observe how soil particles tend to sort by size.

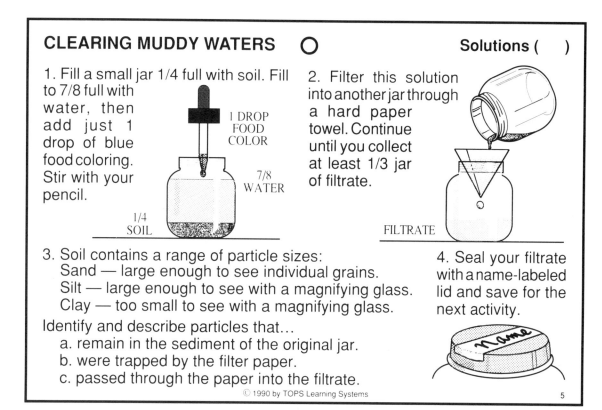

CLEARING MUDDY WATERS ○ Solutions (   )

1. Fill a small jar 1/4 full with soil. Fill to 7/8 full with water, then add just 1 drop of blue food coloring. Stir with your pencil.

1 DROP FOOD COLOR

7/8 WATER

1/4 SOIL

2. Filter this solution into another jar through a hard paper towel. Continue until you collect at least 1/3 jar of filtrate.

FILTRATE

3. Soil contains a range of particle sizes:
Sand — large enough to see individual grains.
Silt — large enough to see with a magnifying glass.
Clay — too small to see with a magnifying glass.
Identify and describe particles that...
a. remain in the sediment of the original jar.
b. were trapped by the filter paper.
c. passed through the paper into the filtrate.

4. Seal your filtrate with a name-labeled lid and save for the next activity.

name

© 1990 by TOPS Learning Systems   5

Answers / Notes

2. The filtrate will take some time to accumulate, collected just a drop at a time. You can speed this drip frequency by holding the filter at the top while another pours in all the solution at once. Don't attempt this without supporting the filter paper at both sides, or using a funnel. Otherwise, the filter will collapse and spill over.

3a. Coarser sand settles to the bottom of the jar, followed by finer silt that collects over the top of it.

CLAY
SILT
SAND

3b. Tiny grains of silt were captured by the filter paper. These can be just barely seen as individual particles with a magnifying glass. As a whole they give the filter paper a dirty brown appearance. The residue itself is fine enough to feel smooth rather than gritty.

3c. Clay passed through the filter paper, along with the food coloring, to form a cloudy blue filtrate. The particles are too small to see individually or to feel gritty. *(If the soil contains any floating organic matter (humus), it too will float away on top of the liquid and be trapped by the filter paper.)*

4. Students should not dispose of their muddy sediments in the sink. Provide a bucket or other container to collect this material for return to its place of origin.

Materials

☐ Two baby food jars and a lid. Students may require masking tape to identify the lid with their name.
☐ Soil. Most any kind of soil will form the desired coarse suspension and colloidal dispersion. Loamy soil is most desirable because it contains a wide range of particle sizes, from sand to clay. Avoid clean sand with no clay.
☐ Food coloring. Blue is not a mandatory color, but easier for partially color blind students to recognize. This is often sold in it own convenient dropping bottle. If not, transfer it to one for convenient, controlled dispensing.
☐ School-grade paper towel.
☐ Scissors and a magnifying glass.
☐ A bucket or large container (optional). See note 4.

(TO) coagulate a colloidal clay dispersion in water with aluminum salt so it may be cleared by filtration.

COAGULATION　　　　　O　　　　　Solutions ( )

1. Add a pinch of alum to your jar of blue filtrate. Stir with your pencil.

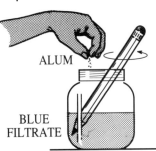

ALUM

BLUE
FILTRATE

2. Filter half this water into a clean jar, then compare it to your original solution. Record your observations, then continue to filter the rest.

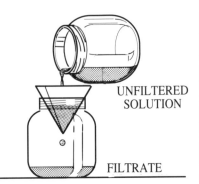

UNFILTERED
SOLUTION

FILTRATE

3. Alum, an aluminum salt, *coagulates* (lumps together) a colloidal dispersion of clay into larger particles.

　　a. How did this work to clear your solution?

　　b. Seal your filtered water with a name-labeled lid and set aside for 24 hours. If coagulation continues, how might this solution look different tomorrow?

　　　　6

Answers / Notes

2. The filtrate is clearer than the original unfiltered solution.

3a. The alum coagulated the dispersed clay particles together, making them large enough to be trapped by the filter paper.

3b. If this coagulation process continues, clay that is still suspended in solution should continue to lump together and settle to the bottom.

Students who finish early should skip ahead to activity 8, constructing the solar still in steps 1 and 2, if possible. After 24 hours they will be ready to both chlorinate their water (activity 7) and evaluate the performance of their solar still (activity 8).

Materials

☐ The cloudy blue filtered water from the previous experiment in a sealed jar.
☐ An additional baby food jar.
☐ School-grade paper towel.
☐ Scissors.
☐ Alum.

(TO) treat water with chlorine bleach. To understand that this kills bacteria but fails to remove other dissolved toxins.

PURIFY BY CHLORINATION   Solutions (   )

1. Gently pour off most of your blue liquid into a clean jar. Are any traces of sediment left behind in what remains? Evaluate your prediction from the previous experiment.
2. Examine the clear-blue liquid you poured off.
   a. Is this water free of suspended particles? How do you know?
   b. What dissolved substances does it contain for sure?
   c. What other dissolved substances might it contain?
3. Water treatment plants usually add chlorine to the public water supply to kill off harmful bacteria. Rinse your empty jar of sediment, then add just enough clear blue water to cover the bottom. Disinfect with a dropper full of chlorine bleach.

ADD 1 DROPPERFUL BLEACH

JUST COVER BOTTOM

   a. What changes can you notice?
   b. Does the water look clear? Is it fit to drink? Explain.
   c. When toxic waste is "thrown away", does it really "go away"?
4. Seal your remaining blue solution with a name-labeled lid and save.

© 1990 by TOPS Learning Systems   7

Introduction

Discuss the purity of your local water supply. Where does it come from? What possible industrial or agricultural contaminants might enter your drinking water between its source and your tap?

Answers / Notes

1. Students should evaluate their predictions from step 3b in the previous activity. Coagulation should have continued overnight, yielding a clear-blue solution with traces of sediment left behind at the bottom of the jar after the liquid was poured off.

2a. This solution is now free of suspended particles because it looks completely clear.
2b. Food coloring and excess alum remaining after coagulation are both dissolved in solution.
2c. If your water is hard, it most certainly contains dissolved calcium and magnesium salts. Depending on water pollution in your area, it might further contain industrial or agricultural contaminates. Encourage your students to speculate, basing their remarks on your introductory discussion.

3. *Students should bleach only a small amount of water, no more than covers the bottom of the jar. Otherwise it will not immediately turn colorless.*
3a. The blue food coloring has faded, producing an uncolored solution.
3b. The water looks clear but it is not fit to drink. It contains food coloring, alum and bleach for sure, possibly other contaminates as well. And it smells bad!
3c. Nothing can ever be thrown "away". All discards remain in toxic or nontoxic forms to affect our environment — the air we breath, the food we eat, the water we drink.

Materials

☐ The clear blue coagulated water in a sealed jar from the previous activity.
☐ An additional baby food jar.
☐ Chlorine bleach. Add this full strength to dropping bottles for student use. Label it properly, warning students to avoid contact with fingers or clothing.

(TO) build a simple solar distillation apparatus that will purify a true solution.

PURIFY BY DISTILLATION Solutions ( )

1. Trim a small paper cup about 2 cm high, to fit inside a small clean jar, resting on its side. Line the lid, plus about 1/4 of a side, with aluminum foil.

2. Fill the cup with just enough of your colored solution to cover the bottom. Seal it inside the jar, being careful not to spill. Set the jar foil-side down in a sunny window or outside in direct sunlight.

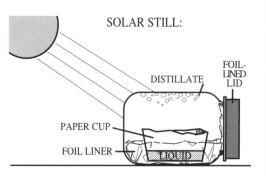

3. Write about your solar still while you are waiting for it to purify your water.
    a. Will your *distillate* be free of dissolved food coloring? Explain.
    b. Draw a diagram explaining how your solar still works. Label your drawing with terms like *condensation* and *evaporation*.
    c. Compare purification by distillation with other water purification processes you have studied.

4. Explain how distillation happens naturally to purify the water we drink.

8

Answers / Notes

3a. Yes. Drops of distillate condensing on the sides of the jar are perfectly clear, free of the blue food coloring that is still dissolved in the true solution. *(This distillate, in fact, is free of all non-volatile solutes. If the solution contained alcohol or some other volatile liquid, it would be driven off first, collecting in the distillate before the water.)*

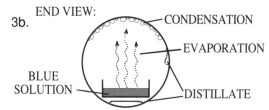

3c. Distillation effectively removes both dissolved and undissolved contaminates from water. Unfortunately it happens quite slowly and requires a lot of energy. Filtering the water, or allowing it to clear by settling, is fast and energy efficient, but fails to remove dissolved contaminants and colloidal dispersions. A coagulating agent like alum will clump and settle certain dispersions, but some alum remains dissolved in the water. Adding chlorine removes nothing from the water but kills harmful bacteria.

4. Water evaporates from oceans, rivers and lakes to condense in the atmosphere and fall back to earth as rain or snow. If this precipitation doesn't encounter air-born pollutants, it will be pure and wonderful, ready to drink.

Extension

There are many other ways to improve water quality. You can aerate it, pass it through activated charcoal, add chemicals that soften it, run it through an ion exchange, use reverse osmosis…. Even freezing it will help! Study one of these processes in depth and write a report.

Materials

☐ A small drinking cup. A small styrofoam cup cut to size may squash fit inside a baby food jar. A plastic film canister cut to size or a small bottle lid will also serve.
☐ A metric ruler (optional).
☐ Scissors and aluminum foil.
☐ A baby food jar and lid.
☐ The clear blue water in a sealed jar saved from the previous activity.
☐ Sunlight (optional). The solar still works fastest and most efficiently in direct sunlight. Appreciable condensation also forms under cloudy daylight conditions if the still is allowed to collect this reduced radiation over several hours. If your classroom has no outside windows, set the still near a light bulb until condensation forms. The quickest way to demonstrate purification by distillation is to simply boil a test tube of water, and point out the clear condensation that forms on the side of the test tube.

(TO) understand the role of refracted light in revealing the interface between phases of different densities. To observe how detergent forms an emulsion in oil.

OIL AND WATER ○   Solutions ( )

1. Fill a test tube 1/2 full of water, then add a dropper full of clean mineral oil. Write your observations.

2. Even though air, glass, mineral oil and water are all transparent, you can still see the surface boundary of each material. This is because light refracts and reflects (bends and bounces) at each interface.

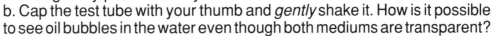

   a. Through what mediums do each of these light ray pass to the eye?
   b. Cap the test tube with your thumb and *gently* shake it. How is it possible to see oil bubbles in the water even though both mediums are transparent?
   c. Shake the tube vigorously. Why does the water look cloudy? Why does it clear up again?

3. Add 1 drop of detergent to your test tube and shake vigorously.
   a. Write your observations.
   b. Detergent *emulsifies* oil by surrounding the tiny drops so they can no longer grow back together. How do emulsions clean greasy (oily) dishes?

9

Answers / Notes

1. The oil floats in a separate layer above the water.

2a. v. air-glass-air-glass-air
    w. air-glass-air-oil-glass-air
    x. air-glass-oil-glass-air
    y. air-glass-water-oil-glass-air
    z. air-glass-water-glass-air

2b. The oil bubbles are clearly visible because light is refracted and reflected at the oil-water interface surrounding each bubble.

2c. Both the water and oil layers cloud over as the oil bubbles decrease in size and become dispersed throughout. Like particles in a suspension, these bubbles are small enough to scatter light. Both the water and oil phases clear up as these oil bubbles rise and join back together, growing in size to where they can again be seen individually. (*Solutions also clear as suspended particles* diminish *in size to the point where they no longer scatter light. This happens when starch is boiled and filtered. The molecules remaining in the filtrate are too small to scatter light, so the solution looks clear.*)

3a. Both the water and oil layers cloud over as before, with thick suds above. The water gradually clears as oil bubbles slowly rise to the bottom of the oil phase, but this oil phase remains permanently clouded. The oil bubbles do not regroup and grow as before.

3b. Liquid detergent divides and conquers. It breaks the grease and oil into an emulsion of tiny droplets, surrounding each one in detergent so it can't regroup and grow in size. As tiny isolated drops, the grease and oil cleanly rinse off dishes, floating away in a water suspension.

Materials

☐ A test tube.
☐ Mineral oil dispensed in a dropping bottle. Any uncolored oil is suitable.
☐ Liquid detergent dispensed in a dropping bottle. A small sample-sized bottle of detergent may be substituted if it has a drip spout.

(TO) understand why salt and water lose volume when mixed together.

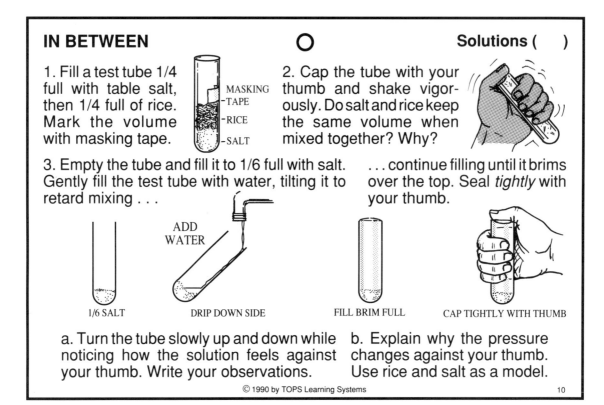

IN BETWEEN O **Solutions ( )**

1. Fill a test tube 1/4 full with table salt, then 1/4 full of rice. Mark the volume with masking tape.

MASKING TAPE
RICE
SALT

2. Cap the tube with your thumb and shake vigorously. Do salt and rice keep the same volume when mixed together? Why?

3. Empty the tube and fill it to 1/6 full with salt. Gently fill the test tube with water, tilting it to retard mixing . . .

. . . continue filling until it brims over the top. Seal *tightly* with your thumb.

ADD WATER

1/6 SALT   DRIP DOWN SIDE   FILL BRIM FULL   CAP TIGHTLY WITH THUMB

a. Turn the tube slowly up and down while noticing how the solution feels against your thumb. Write your observations.

b. Explain why the pressure changes against your thumb. Use rice and salt as a model.

© 1990 by TOPS Learning Systems   10

Answers / Notes

2. The level of the salt plus rice drops perhaps 1 cm below the masking tape when both are mixed together. The salt fills the empty spaces between the rice grains and thus the mixture takes up less space.

3a. The pressure drops, pulling the thumb gently into the mouth of the test tube! *(This is a subtle yet obvious effect. To successfully observe it (a) the water must be added as directed, to avoid premature mixing and (b) all air should be displaced from the tube before it is capped with the thumb.)*

3b. The salt grains filled empty spaces between the rice grains, causing the mixture to lose volume. In a similar manner, the dissolving salt entered intermolecular sites between the water molecules to reduce the overall volume of the solution, thus creating a slight vacuum. *(Encourage students to talk about ions, not molecules. Sugar dissolves into water as molecules; but salt ionizes into positive sodium ions and negative chlorine ions.)*

Materials

☐ A dry test tube. If it is wet, tape a small piece of paper towel on the end of a straw. Twist the towel inside the bottom of the tube to soak up any moisture.
☐ Fine-grained table salt.
☐ Rice.
☐ Masking tape.
☐ A metric ruler (optional).
☐ Scissors.
☐ A small beaker (optional). Use this to pour water into the tilted tube, or add a stream of water directly from the tap.

(TO) observe how light bends as alcohol dissolves in water. To explain the reduction in volume as these liquids form a solution.

ALCOHOL AND WATER ○   Solutions (   )

1. Fill a clean test tube 1/2 full with water. Hold it up to good light, then *gently* drip rubbing alcohol down the tilted side of the glass until it is almost full. Rest the test tube in a jar while you write your observations.

ALCOHOL

OBSERVE CAREFULLY...

WATER

2. Hold the test tube with graph paper in the distant background. Do you see evidence of more than 1 phase (layer) in your test tube? Explain.

ALCOHOL

WATER

3. *Predict* how the solution will feel against your thumb as you tip the test tube up and down to mix the solution. Give reasons for your answer.

4. Test your prediction. Top off the tube with alcohol and cap it tightly shut with your thumb so no air is trapped.

5. Did the phases really mix together? How do you know?

TILT UP AND DOWN

© 1990 by TOPS Learning Systems   11

Answers / Notes

1. At first a wavy turbulence is created as the drops of alcohol mix with water. Gradually, a level of alcohol is established over the water which buffers additional drops from mixing in. *(This turbulence is sometimes called the Schlieren effect, and is associated with the dissolving process.)*

2. Yes. Light is refracted as it travels between the alcohol phase and the water phase. Graph paper lines in the background are distorted at this interface. *(Actually 3 phases are present, pure alcohol on top, pure water below, and a mixed alcohol-water phase in between. The height of this middle phase depends on how gently the alcohol was added to the water.)*

3. The dissolving alcohol and water may lose volume as one liquid dissolves into the intermolecular spaces of the other. This would reduced the volume of liquid in the test tube somewhat, and create a slight vacuum or inward pressure on the thumb.

4. As predicted, the total volume in the test tube decreased to create a definite suction on the thumb. *(Students may notice as well that the alcohol dissolves endothermically, cooling noticeably as it absorbs energy from its surroundings.)*

5. Yes, additional water and alcohol mixed together. This is apparent because a wavy turbulence was again observed as the two phases mixed. Afterwards only a single water-alcohol phase remains. The background graph line are no longer distorted as before.

Materials

☐ A test tube. Small test tubes will conserve rubbing alcohol.

☐ Rubbing alcohol dispensed in a dropping bottle. This is sold in drug stores as 70% ethyl or isopropyl alcohol by volume. Pure lab-quality alcohol of low molecular weight will work even better. Denatured alcohol is poisonous and should carry an appropriate warning label.

☐ A baby food jar.

☐ Graph paper. Photocopy the supplementary grid at the back of this book. Save it to use later as well.

(TO) review three purifying techniques studied thus far. To distinguish between coarse suspensions, colloidal dispersions and true solutions.

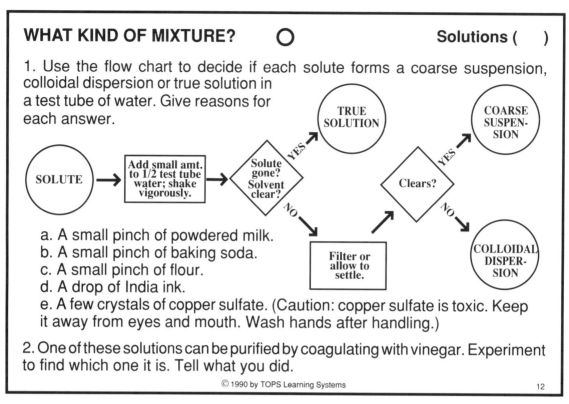

WHAT KIND OF MIXTURE?   ○   **Solutions ( )**

1. Use the flow chart to decide if each solute forms a coarse suspension, colloidal dispersion or true solution in a test tube of water. Give reasons for each answer.

SOLUTE → Add small amt. to 1/2 test tube water; shake vigorously. → Solute gone? Solvent clear? — YES → TRUE SOLUTION — NO → Filter or allow to settle. → Clears? — YES → COARSE SUSPENSION — NO → COLLOIDAL DISPERSION

a. A small pinch of powdered milk.
b. A small pinch of baking soda.
c. A small pinch of flour.
d. A drop of India ink.
e. A few crystals of copper sulfate. (Caution: copper sulfate is toxic. Keep it away from eyes and mouth. Wash hands after handling.)

2. One of these solutions can be purified by coagulating with vinegar. Experiment to find which one it is. Tell what you did.

© 1990 by TOPS Learning Systems   12

Answers / Notes

1a. Powdered milk forms a COLLOIDAL DISPERSION in water. The solution remains cloudy, even after filtration.

1b. Baking soda forms a TRUE SOLUTION in water. The solute disappears and the solution remains clear. *(Students who add too much will saturate the water and observe that the excess forms a coarse suspension.)*

1c. Flour forms a COARSE SUSPENSION in water. The cloudy solution clears when filtered.

1d. India ink forms a COLLOIDAL DISPERSION in water. The darkened solution is not cleared by filtration. *(It is also possible to conclude that India ink forms a true solution, since its is only marginally opaque.)*

1e. Copper sulfate forms a TRUE SOLUTION in water. The solute gradually disappears, turning the water clear blue. *(It is important to note that the copper sulfate colors the water, but it does not make it cloudy or opaque like a suspension.)*

2. Vinegar coagulates India ink. This was discovered through a process of elimination. Originally the India ink solution passed through filter paper to blacken the filtrate. After adding vinegar, the fine particles of India ink lumped together, producing a coarse suspension that cleared both by settling, and filtration.

Materials

☐ Test tubes. Each lab group needs a minimum of two. Hold them in a baby food jar or beaker.
☐ A packet of powdered milk.
☐ A box of baking soda with a spoon for easy dispensing.
☐ A small container of flour, bleached or unbleached.
☐ India ink dispensed in a dropper bottle. This is sold in stationery stores or art supply stores.
☐ A bottle of copper sulfate. Include a plastic spoon for easy dispensing. This is sold in drug stores, probably in the traditional home chemical section, next to the alum and Epsom salt. You may also find it in gardening stores. Copper sulfate is irritating to the skin and eyes and poisonous if consumed. The bottle must carry a suitable warning label.
☐ School-grade paper towels.
☐ Scissors.
☐ Vinegar. Find this in any grocery store. Dispense it in a dropping bottle.

(TO) discover how temperature influences the rate of dissolving. To distinguish between heterogeneous and homogeneous mixing.

HOT AND COLD   ○   Solutions (   )

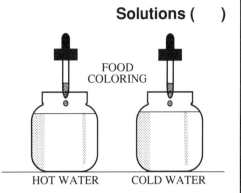

1. Fill one jar with hot water; another with cold.

2. Wait one minute for the water to calm, then add just 1 drop of food coloring to each.
   a. Record your observations over the next few minutes. (Don't move the jars.)
   b. How does temperature seem to affect the rate of mixing?

3. Stir the warm solution (if it is not mixed already). Leave the cool solution alone.

   a. How is the hot *homogeneous* solution different than the cold *heterogeneous* one?
   b. Draw a dot sketch of each solution. Use more dots to indicate areas of high food-coloring concentration, fewer dots to show areas of lower concentration.
   c. True solutions are clear and homogeneous. Does food coloring form a true solution in water?

13

Answers / Notes

2a. The food coloring mixes throughout both jars without stirring. This happens more rapidly in the hot water than in the cold. The blue drop tends to spread over the surface of the hot water first, before sinking, but sinks directly to the bottom of the cold water. The swirling marble-like patterns left behind have clear distinct boundaries at first, then become diffuse over time. A greater concentration of blue remains at the bottom of each jar, more in the cold water than in the hot.

2b. The higher the temperature, the faster the rate of mixing.

3a. The homogeneous solution has a uniform blue color throughout, showing that the food coloring is mixed evenly in the water. The heterogeneous solution, by contrast, contains a complex pattern of light and dark blue, indicating uneven concentrations throughout a solution that is not yet thoroughly mixed.

3c. Yes. The solution is not cloudy, and homogeneous after mixing.

3b.
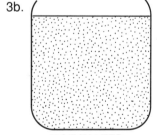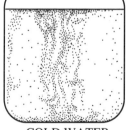

HOT WATER   COLD WATER

Materials

☐ Two baby food jars.
☐ Hot and cold water. You might be able to use water directly from the tap. The hot water should be dishwashing temperature (near 50° C) or warmer. The cool water should be lower than room temperature (below 20° C), near freezing if possible. If your don't have piped-in hot water, students might heat their own in Pyrex beakers. Or you can heat it in a pot using a portable hot plate.
☐ Blue food coloring dispensed in a dropper bottle.

(TO) geometrically demonstrate how the surface area of a solute increases as its crystals are subdivided into smaller particles. To understand why pulverizing the solute accelerates its dissolving rate.

PARTICLE SIZE ⭕ Solutions ( )

1. Cut out a centimeter cube pattern. Fold and tape it together with small slices of clear tape.

2. This whole "salt" cube measures 1 cm on a side. How many cubes would result if it were subdivided into…
    a. smaller cubes that measure .5 cm on a side?
    b. tiny cubes that measure .1 cm on a side?

3. Remember that a cube has 6 sides. What is the total surface area of… a. the single b. the several c. the many
         1 cm cube? .5 cm cubes? .1 cm cubes?

4. Dissolving happens only at the surface of a crystal where water molecules directly contact the salt. When salt crystals are crushed into finer particles, how might this affect the rate of dissolving? Explain.

5. Test your hypothesis.
    a. Pour 1 mL of rock salt between scratch paper folded into quarters. Crush it with a small jar.
    b. Leave another 1 mL portion of rock salt uncrushed.
    c. Compare their dissolving times in test tubes half full of water. Did particle size make a difference?

© 1990 by TOPS Learning Systems   14

Answers / Notes

2a. There are 8 cubes measuring .5 cm on a side. (2 x 2 x 2)
2b. There are 1000 cubes measuring .1 cm on a side. (10 x 10 x 10)

3. *These computations are simple, but require some knowledge of areas and decimals.*
3a. The total surface area of the single 1 cm cube is 6 cm^2.
3b. The total surface area of all eight .5 cm cubes is 12 cm^2. (8 x 6 x .5 x .5)
3c. The total surface area of all thousand .1 cm cubes is 60 cm^2. (1000 x 6 x .1 x .1)

4. Crushing the salt into smaller particles increases the surface area that will come into direct contact with water. Thus it can be expected to dissolve more rapidly.

5c. Yes. The crushed rock salt dissolved faster than the uncrushed rock salt.

Materials

☐ Scissors.
☐ A centimeter cube pattern. Photocopy the pattern from the back of this book.
☐ Clear tape.
☐ A dry 10 mL graduate. Dry the inside with a straw and paper towel as necessary. See Materials, note 10.
☐ Rock salt. This is sold in grocery stores specifically for making ice cream. You'll probably have to purchase a 5 pound bag, though you can get by with much less.
☐ Scratch paper.
☐ A dry baby food jar.
☐ Test tubes.
☐ A wall clock or wrist watch with a second hand (optional).

(TO) recognize that solvents have a saturation point beyond which more solute will not readily dissolve.

SATURATION **Solutions ( )**

1. Fill a test tube 1/4 full with baking soda, then add water to 7/8 full. Cap with your thumb and shake vigorously at least 100 times.

2. Filter the baking soda water into another clean test tube. Did it form a…
    a. coarse suspension? Explain.
    b. true solution? Explain.

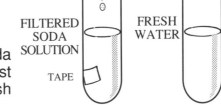

FILTERED SODA SOLUTION

FRESH WATER

TAPE

3. Tag the test tube of filtered baking soda water with a piece of tape. Rinse the other test tube and fill with an equal amount of fresh water. Will a pinch of baking soda…
    a. dissolve in the filtered soda solution? Write your observations.
    b. dissolve in the fresh water? Write your observations.

4. The baking soda water is *saturated,* while the original pure water is now *unsaturated.* What do these terms mean?

5. Add 1 drop of food coloring to each tube. Don't stir.
    a. Draw how the drop interacts with each solution.
    b. Why does the food coloring sink in one liquid but float in the other?

15

Answers / Notes

2. *Baby food jars make ideal test tube holders.*
2a. Yes. Excess baking soda formed a coarse suspension because it was originally cloudy, but cleared with filtration.
2b. Yes. It was previously determined (activity 12, step 1b) that baking soda dissolves in water to from a true solution.
3a. No. After vigorously shaking the solute remains in the bottom of the test tube.
3b. Yes. After vigorous shaking the solute dissolved, forming a clear true solution.

4. In a saturated solution, the solvent holds all the solute it possibly can. No more will dissolve. In an unsaturated solution there is still room between the solvent molecules to dissolve additional solute.

5a.

SATURATED UNSATURATED

5b. The saturated solution contains more of the heavy solute than the less concentrated unsaturated solution. This makes it more dense, causing the lighter food coloring to float above it.

Materials

☐ Baking soda. It is difficult to transfer baking soda (and other salts in this module) from a spoon to a test tube without creating a minor mess. Demonstrate how to transfer the salt onto a folded quarter sheet of scratch paper, then pour it cleanly into the test tube down the fold.

FOLDED PAPER

☐ Two test tubes.
☐ School-grade paper towels.
☐ Scissors.
☐ A baby food jar (optional). See note 2.
☐ Masking tape.
☐ Food coloring.

(TO) compare the dissolving capacity of saturated salt water with fresh water.

CAN MORE DISSOLVE?　　　○　　　　　Solutions ( )

1. Fill a test tube 1/4 full of rock salt, then add water to 7/8 full. Shake vigorously at least 100 times to saturate the solution.

2. Use this salt solution plus fresh water to do each experiment. Predict what you think will happen first, before you try it.

a. Add quarter pieces of seltzer tablets to each test tube.

b. Add a pinch of baking soda to each test tube.

c. Pool a dropperful of each liquid on inverted jars. Rest sugar cubes in each puddle.

SALT WATER　FRESH WATER　　SALT WATER　FRESH WATER　　SALT WATER　FRESH WATER

3. Evaluate your predictions.
4. In each case, explain why salt water has a different effect than fresh water?

© 1990 by TOPS Learning Systems　　　　　16

Answers / Notes

2a. The seltzer tablets should dissolve faster in the fresh water than in the salt water. *(The tablets are broken into quarters so they fit inside the test tubes. Smaller tablets may not require breaking.)*

2b. The baking soda will dissolve and disappear into the fresh water, but remain at the bottom of the test tube of salt water, at least partly undissolved.

2c. The sugar cube will collapse as it dissolves into the fresh water puddle. This happens more slowly in the salt water puddle. *(At first it may look like nothing will happen to either cube. Then both will collapse, the one soaking up fresh water much more rapidly than the one soaking up salt water.)*

3. Students should report any discrepancy between what they predicted and what they actually observed.

4. The seltzer tablets, baking soda and sugar cube all dissolve into the fresh water most rapidly, because the intermolecular sites between the water molecules are not yet occupied with salt *(sodium and chlorine ions)*.

Materials

☐ Three test tubes.
☐ Rock salt. Do not substitute table salt. It usually contains additives that cloud the water.
☐ Seltzer tablets. Any solid that fizzes in water, like Alka-Seltzer, should work.
☐ Baking soda.
☐ An eye dropper.
☐ Baby food jars. If you are using flat-bottomed beakers, substitute laboratory watch glasses.
☐ Sugar cubes.

(TO) examine rapid crystal growth on a microscope slide. To recognize the basic repeating pattern.

FROSTED GLASS ○   Solutions (   )

1. Fill a test tube 1/5 full with Epsom salt. Add water to *just* cover the salt, then shake vigorously 100 times.

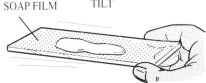

    a. Did you make a saturated solution? Explain.
    b. Comment on the solubility of Epsom salt in water.

2. Rub a drop of detergent over a clean, dry microscope slide. Wipe it off with tissue to leave a dry film.

3. Wet this slide with a few drops of your saturated solution, tipping it to spread the liquid. Hold the slide by its edge, so you don't touch the surface. Let any excess run onto the tissue.

4. Fan the slide with a piece of paper. When crystals start to form around the edges, hold the slide up to some good light and observe with a magnifying glass.

    a. Sketch the crystal patterns you observe.
    b. Identify the basic repeating unit in an Epsom salt crystal.
    c. Why doesn't this salt remain in solution? What makes it crystallize?

17

Answers / Notes

1a. Yes. After vigorous shaking, undissolved Epsom salt still remains at the bottom of the test tube. Little, if any, additional salt can dissolve, because the water is already near saturation.

1b. Epsom salt is highly soluble in water. The water barely covered the undissolved salt to start, and now very little remains undissolved.

4. *The slide will not dry by blowing on it. Water vapor in your breath will actually redissolve crystals that have already formed.*
    For a really spectacular show, examine the slide under a microscope at 50 power!

4a.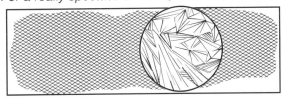

4b. The "frosted" microscope slide is really a repeating array of needle-like crystals growing outward in many different directions, often from a common point.

4c. The dissolved salt must crystallize because water slowly evaporates from the surface of the slide.

Materials

☐ A test tube. A baby food jar or beaker makes a convenient holder.
☐ Epsom salt. Find this in a drug store, next to the alum and copper sulfate.
☐ Liquid detergent.
☐ A microscope slide.
☐ A toilet tissue.
☐ A magnifying glass.
☐ A microscope (optional).

(TO) grow crystals from saturated salt solutions. To identify the basic repeating crystal shapes.

BASIC SHAPES   Solutions ( )

1. Rubber band 3 inverted jars together.
     Label with these 3 salts:

2. Make saturated solutions of each salt.
     a. Fill a test tube to 1/5 full with a salt, then add warm water to 2/5 full.
     b. Shake vigorously at least 100 times.
     c. Allow excess salt to settle, then pour off a *clear* puddle of the saturated solution onto the bottom of each labeled jar. (CAUTION: Copper sulfate is toxic. Keep away from eyes and mouth. Wash hands after use.)

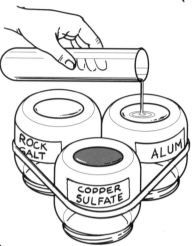

3. Set the liquids aside to evaporate overnight.
     a. Sketch the crystals that have formed on each jar.
     b. Identify the most basic repeating crystal shape for each salt.
     c. If crystals contain the same basic shape why don't the larger ones all look the same?

18

Answers / Notes

2c. The excess rock salt and copper sulfate crystals are large enough to settle quickly, allowing the solution to be poured off immediately. But alum crystals are much smaller. Students should wait several minutes to allow excess alum to settle, or they should filter the solution onto the jar bottom.

3a.

3b. Rock salt grows in cubes. A square stairstep pattern sometimes leads into the center of the larger cubes.

Copper sulfate crystals are shaped like 3-dimensional parallelograms.

Alum forms tiny distinct crystals. Careful observation reveals that many are hexagonal in shape.

3c. The larger crystals share a similarity of form, but each has a unique shape. This unique shape depends on the orientation and size of its smaller unit shapes and how they fit together. A large collection of cubes, for example, forms a rounded pile, even though each smaller cube is perfectly formed.

Materials

☐ A rubber band. Use a wide one or several narrow ones.
☐ Baby food jars. If you are using flat-bottomed beakers, substitute laboratory watch glasses.
☐ Copper sulfate.
☐ Rock salt.
☐ Alum.
☐ A test tube.
☐ Warm running water from a tap (optional). Warm water is better than either hot or cold water because it leaves the largest crystals behind after it evaporates. If you don't have warm water piped in, use room temperature water.
☐ A magnifying glass.

(TO) analyze various sources of drinking water for the presence of dissolved minerals.

WATER SPOTS ◯ **Solutions (   )**

1. Examine a jar of fresh tap water. Just by looking at the water, can you tell if it is really pure?

2. Place a drop of tap water on a perfectly clean microscope slide. Evaporate the water to dryness in a breeze or near a heat source. Then hold it up to some good light.
   a. What can you observe?
   b. Could tap water be called a true solution? Why?

TAP WATER

3. Repeat the analysis with water from other sources: bottled spring water, river water, aquarium water, distilled water, etc. Report your findings.

19

Answers / Notes

1. No. The tap water may be a crystal-clear, true solution containing significant concentrations of dissolved minerals.

2a. The water leaves behind a definite spot.
2b. Yes. It forms a clear solution that contains dissolved minerals.

3. Water from all sources will likely spot a clean microscope slide, even distilled water. *The water spot test is very sensitive. If distilled water leaves a spot, point out that these trace minerals dissolved* after *the distillation process. No salts carry over in pure steam.*

BOTTLED DRINKING WATER

DISTILLED WATER

Materials

☐ A baby food jar.
☐ A perfectly clean microscope slide.
☐ An eye dropper.
☐ A breeze or heat source to evaporate the water drop. A heating vent may work in cold weather. In warm weather, try an open window with a breeze. A candle or Bunsen burner flame will also quickly evaporate the drop while the other end is held by hand. If you opt for this method, caution students to heat the slide gently (to avoid cracking) and allow plenty of time for the slide to cool down. (Hot glass looks cool.)
☐ Other sources of water — bottled drinking water, distilled water, water from a local stream, etc.
☐ Cleanser (optional). Water spots formed over a candle or Bunsen burner will be baked on hard. Scouring with cleanser may be necessary to fully clean the slide.

(TO) model equilibrium conditions in a saturated solution. To appreciate, on a molecular level, the dynamic nature of saturated solutions.

EQUILIBRIUM   O   **Solutions ( )**

1. Trace the mouth of a jar on an index card, then cut out the circle. Punch 4 holes near the edge like this:

2. Add just enough rice to cover the bottom of a jar. Invert a second jar over the first, sandwiching the punched circle between. Seal the rims together with masking tape.

TAPE

RICE

3. Cut out an "equilibrium strip" and tape it like this:

4. Shake all rice grains to the left, then hold the jars sideways. Shake the jars vigorously 10 times and look; shake 10 more times and look.... Repeat until you no longer see any change:

CRYSTALLIZED SALT ⇄ DISSOLVED SALT

EQUILIBRIUM STRIP

    a. This models what happens when you dump excess rock salt into a glass of water and half of it dissolves. Explain.
    b. *Equilibrium* means "change forward = change back." Does your model suggest that salt and water reach equilibrium right away?
    c. At equilibrium, excess salt in water appears *static* (there are no visible changes). Does your model suggest that this true for each *atom* of salt?

     20

Answers / Notes

4a. When excess rock salt is first added to water, all of the salt is in its crystal form: this is modeled by all the rice being confined to the left jar. Over time half dissolves: with every 10 shakes, more rice accumulates in the right jar until there are equal amounts on both sides.

4b. No. In the beginning more rice "dissolves" right than "crystalizes" left. These shifts equalize over time as equal amounts of rice accumulate in both jars.

4c. No. At equilibrium, no additional rock salt appears to dissolve: equal amounts of rice remain in both jars no matter how long you shake them. Individual atoms of rock salt still "dissolve" and "crystalize" however: rice grains continue to pass at equal rates between both jars, with no overall change.

Discussion

• Use the jars to model the effect of adding just a pinch of rock salt to a glassful of water. (Begin will all the rice in the "crystalized" jar, then turn it upside down and shake all the rice into the "dissolved" jar. This reaction goes to completion.)

• Model the effects of adding excess rock salt to a glassful of *hot* water. (Begin will all the rice in the "crystalized" jar, then shake it sideways, but with a downward tilt toward the "dissolved" jar. A state of equilibrium results with more rice to the right than to the left.)

• Model the effects of adding excess rock salt to a glassful of *cold* water. (Similar to the hot water demonstration, only tilt the jars toward the "crystalized" side as you shake them.)

Materials

☐ Baby food jars.
☐ An index card.
☐ Scissors.
☐ A paper punch.
☐ Rice.
☐ Masking tape.
☐ An "equilibrium strip" photocopied from the back of this book.

(TO) graph how rock salt dissolves as a function of time. To observe that the rate of dissolving slows as the solution approaches its point of saturation.

RATE OF DISSOLVING (1) Solutions ( )

1. Gently tap down 5 mL of rock salt in a *dry* 10 mL graduate. Pour it all onto a creased piece of paper.

2. Rinse the graduate and fill it with exactly 10 g of fresh water. How do you know you measured out 10 g?

3. Start timing on a clock or stop watch as you pour all the salt back into the 10 mL graduate of water.

4. Seal the graduate with your thumb and *slowly* tilt it up and down, stopping to record the new salt level (in column 2 of the table) after each half-minute interval. Always tap the side of the graduate to level and settle the salt inside.

5. Calculate in column 3 the amount of salt dissolved after each time interval.

6. Graph time (col. 1) vs. the amount dissolved (col. 3). Interpret your graph line.

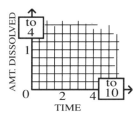

time (min)	salt level (mL)	amount dissolved (mL salt/10 g H$_2$0)
0	5.0	0
1/2		
1		
1 1/2		
2		
3		
4		
6		
10		

© 1990 by TOPS Learning Systems   21

Answers / Notes

2. The density of water is 1 g/mL, so 10 mL has a mass of 10 g.

4-5. *Review how to accurately read a 10 mL graduated cylinder. Point out that each small division represents .2 mL, not .1 mL.*

Since the rate of dissolving is influenced by how rapidly the solution is agitated, remind students to keep this variable constant. They should slowly invert the test tube at the same speed, perhaps once every 5 seconds. Here is one result:

time (min)	salt level (mL)	amount dissolved (mL salt/10 g H$_2$0)
0	5.0	0
1/2	3.9	1.1
1	3.3	1.7
1 1/2	2.9	2.1
2	2.5	2.5
3	2.2	2.8
4	2.0	3.0
6	1.8	3.2
10	1.7	3.3

6.

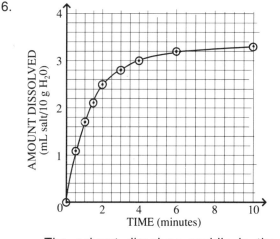

The solvent dissolves rapidly in the beginning, then more and more slowly as the solution approaches saturation.

Materials

☐ A 10 mL graduate.
☐ A paper towel and straw to dry the graduate. See Materials, notes 10.
☐ Rock salt.
☐ A wall clock with a second hand sweep or a stop watch.
☐ Graph paper. Photocopy the grid at the back of this book.

(TO) become familiar with various units of concentration. To graph, in standard units, how a dissolving salt approaches its limit of solubility as a function of time.

RATE OF DISSOLVING (2)   Solutions (   )

1. Gently tap down 10 mL of rock salt in a dry graduate.
   a. Find the mass of this salt on a centered balance.
   b. Calculate the mass of 1 mL of rock salt.

2. Suppose 1 mL of rock salt dissolves in 10 g of water. Express the *concentration* of this solution in…
   a. mL solute/10 g H_2O?   b. g solute/10 g H_2O?   c. g solute/100 g H_2O?

3. Use your data from before to complete column 2. Convert to standard units of concentration (g solute/100 g H_2O) in column 3. Plot column 1 vs. 3 on another graph.

4. Salt forms a saturated solution in water at 36 g/100 g H_2O.
   a. Represent this with a dashed horizontal line on your graph.
   b. Did your rock salt solution reach saturation? Interpret your graph.

time (min)	amount dissolved (mL salt/10 g H₂0)	amount dissolved (g salt/100 g H₂0)
0	0	0
1/2		
1		
1 1/2		
2		
3		
4		
6		
10		

22

Answers / Notes

1. Measurements will vary, depending on the size of the crystals of your particular brand of rock salt.

    1a. 10 mL rock salt = 10.85 g.
    1b. 1 mL rock salt = 1.085 g.

3-4. To complete column 3, students should multiply column 2 by the conversion factor calculated in step 2c.

time (min)	amount dissolved (mL salt/10 g H₂0)	amount dissolved (g salt/100 g H₂0)
0	0	0
1/2	1.1	11.9
1	1.7	18.4
1 1/2	2.1	22.8
2	2.5	27.1
3	2.8	30.4
4	3.0	32.6
6	3.2	34.7
10	3.3	35.8

4b. The graph line approaches 36 g/100 g H_2O, but cannot exceed it, since this is the upper limit of saturation.

2. Students don't need to actually make this solution, although it is instructive to do so. Both 1 mL of salt and 10 g of water should be measured separately. (If salt is added to the graduate and then topped off with water to 10 mL, there will be less than 10 g of water in the graduate.)

2a. 1 mL solute/10 g H_2O
2b. 1.085 g solute/10 g H_2O
2c. 10.85 g solute/100 g H_2O

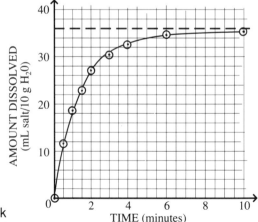

Materials

☐ A 10 mL graduate and rock salt.
☐ An equal-arm balance. The balance constructed in the Task Card Module, *Weighing 05,* is suitable to use here and in all TOPS experiments requiring mass determinations.
☐ A calculator (optional).
☐ Graph paper. Photocopy the grid at the back of this book.

(TO) test various salts for water of hydration.

WATER OF HYDRATION (1) Solutions ( )

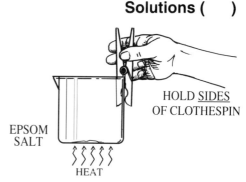

HOLD <u>SIDES</u> OF CLOTHESPIN

EPSOM SALT

HEAT

1. SLOWLY heat a SMALL pinch of Epsom salt in a small Pyrex beaker. (CAUTION: the beaker gets very hot even though it looks cool. Think before you touch!)

    a. Write your observations.

    b. Hydrates contain water as part of their crystal structure. Is Epsom salt a hydrate?

2. Clean the beaker, then test a few crystals of copper sulfate for water of hydration. Write your observations and conclusions. (CAUTION: Heat slowly, as before. Copper sulfate is toxic. Keep it away from your eyes and mouth. Wash your hands after handling.)

3. Repeat this test for rock salt and report your results.

4. Salts with water of hydration driven away are called anhydrous.

    a. Would anhydrous copper sulfate make a good moisture indicator? Why?

    b. Test your hypothesis.

23

Answers / Notes

1. *This experiment requires close teacher supervision of students and strict enforcement of the following safety rules:*

    • *Use only a small pinch of each salt.*
    • *Heat each salt slowly and gently. Rapid heating may cause water in the hydrated salts to superheat, generating pockets of rapidly expanding steam that could explode the crystals.*

    • *Hold the clothespin at its sides, as illustrated above. In this manner students can squeeze it as hard as they like without danger of opening the clothespin and dropping the beaker.*
    • *Allow the beaker plenty of time to cool before touching it with bare skin. Blistering hot glass and cool glass look exactly the same.*

1a. The salt crystals hiss and fizz as they are heated. Water vapor condenses on the side of the beaker.

1b. Yes. Epsom salt is a hydrate. Water was driven off when it was heated.

2. Copper sulfate also contains water of hydration. The crystals changed from blue to white, while water vapor condensed against the side of the beaker.

3. Rock salt crystals did not appear to change in any way as they were heated. Nor was any water vapor given off. Rock salt is not a hydrate.

4a. Anhydrous copper sulfate is white, while the hydrated form is blue. Any change from white to blue, therefore, would indicate the presence of water.

4b. Students should heat a few crystals of copper sulfate in the Pyrex beaker to drive off the water of hydration and obtain the white anhydrous form. Adding water to these crystals will immediately change them back to their hydrated blue form. *(Even without adding water the crystals will gradually turn blue as they absorb water vapor from the air.)*

Materials

☐ Any suitable heat source. Use a hot plate, candle, alcohol lamp or Bunsen burner. Provide matches as necessary.
☐ Epsom salt.

☐ A small Pyrex beaker.
☐ A clothespin to hold the beaker.
☐ Copper sulfate.
☐ Rock salt.

(TO) quantitatively determine how much water of hydration is held by Epsom salt. To compare this experimental value with theoretical values based on its gram formula weight.

WATER OF HYDRATION (2)   ◯   Solutions (   )

1. Weigh out exactly 1 gram of Epsom salt and pour it into a small, clean, Pyrex beaker. Heat thoroughly to drive off the water of hydration.

    a. Allow the beaker to cool *before* you touch the glass! Pour the salt back onto your balance and find its mass again.

    b. Express its loss in mass as a percentage.

$$\% \text{ mass loss} = \frac{\text{original mass - final mass}}{\text{original mass}} \times 100$$

EPSOM SALT

HEAT

2. Epsom salt loses water at 2 different temperatures:

$$MgSO_4 \cdot 7H_2O \xrightarrow{150^\circ C} MgSO_4 \cdot 1H2O \xrightarrow{200^\circ C} MgSO_4$$

    a. Compute its gram formula weight at each temperature.
        (Mg = 24.3 g, S = 32.1 g, O = 16.0 g, H = 1.0 g)
    b. What percentage of mass loss should you observe at each temperature?

3. Compare your experimental and theoretical calculations.

4. Do you think your anhydrous (or partially anhydrous) Epsom salt will gain weight during the next 24 hours? Test your prediction.

© 1990 by TOPS Learning Systems   24

Answers / Notes

1a. Results will vary, depending on the temperature to which the salt is heated, and how long it is maintained at that temperature. These results were obtained on an electric stove element:

1a. The mass of the salt dropped from 1.00 g to .55 g.   1b. % mass loss = $\dfrac{1.00 \text{ g} - .55 \text{ g}}{1.00 \text{ g}} \times 100 = 45\%$

2. The gram formula weight is the mass of 1 mole of magnesium atoms, together with its sulfur, oxygen and hydrogen atoms in the ratios indicated. Just as a dozen is always 12, a mole is always 6.02 x 10²³.

2a. MgSO₄	H₂O	MgSO₄ · 7H₂O (room temperature)	MgSO₄ · 1H₂O (150° C)	MgSO₄ (200°C)
Mg = 24.3 g				
S = 32.1 g	H₂ = 2.0 g	MgSO₄ = 120.4 g	MgSO₄ = 120.4 g	
O₄ = 64.0 g	O = 16.0 g	7H₂O = 7(18.0) = 126.0 g	1H₂O = 18.0 g	
120.4 g	18.0 g	246.4 g	138.4 g	120.4 g

2b. At 150° C:
% mass loss = $\dfrac{246.4 \text{ g} - 138.4 \text{ g}}{246.4 \text{ g}} \times 100 = 44\%$
       At 200° C:
% mass loss = $\dfrac{246.4 \text{ g} - 120.4 \text{ g}}{246.4 \text{ g}} \times 100 = 51\%$

3. Answers will vary depending on how the salt is heated. In our particular example, the 45% mass loss is very close to the predicted value for a loss of 6 water molecules of hydration.

4. Students should first make a prediction, then reweigh their salt the next day to see if they were correct. *(Our particular salt sample regained about half its lost weight the first day, then continued to gain weight on subsequent days until it finally returned to its original 1.00 gram mass.)*

Materials

☐ An equal-arm balance.
☐ Epsom salt.
☐ A small Pyrex beaker and a clothespin to hold it.
☐ Any suitable heat source. Use a candle, alcohol lamp or Bunsen burner plus matches, or a hot plate.

(TO) observe how solubility changes with the nature of the solute and the temperature of the solvent. To describe these changes in both qualitative and quantitative terms.

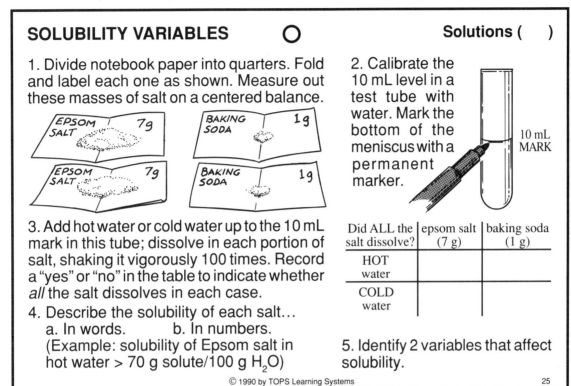

SOLUBILITY VARIABLES ○   Solutions (   )

1. Divide notebook paper into quarters. Fold and label each one as shown. Measure out these masses of salt on a centered balance.

EPSOM SALT   7g
EPSOM SALT   7g
BAKING SODA   1g
BAKING SODA   1g

2. Calibrate the 10 mL level in a test tube with water. Mark the bottom of the meniscus with a permanent marker.

10 mL MARK

3. Add hot water or cold water up to the 10 mL mark in this tube; dissolve in each portion of salt, shaking it vigorously 100 times. Record a "yes" or "no" in the table to indicate whether *all* the salt dissolves in each case.

4. Describe the solubility of each salt…
   a. In words.   b. In numbers.
   (Example: solubility of Epsom salt in hot water > 70 g solute/100 g H$_2$O)

Did ALL the salt dissolve?	epsom salt (7 g)	baking soda (1 g)
HOT water		
COLD water		

5. Identify 2 variables that affect solubility.

© 1990 by TOPS Learning Systems   25

Introduction

Solubility describes the amount of salt that dissolves in water.

IN WORDS, solubility is described as: very soluble, moderately soluble, slightly soluble, insoluble.

Describe the solubility of sand in water (insoluble); limestone in water (slightly soluble); sugar in water (very soluble).

IN NUMBERS, solubility is described as that concentration (g solute/100 g H$_2$O) which forms a saturated solution at a specific temperature.

It is determined that 3.2 grams of copper sulfate (but no more) will dissolve in 10 g of water at 20° C. What is its solubility? (32 g/100 g H$_2$O at 20° C) When this solution is heated to 30° C, an additional .6 grams of copper sulfate will dissolve. What is its new solubility? (38 g/100 g H$_2$O at 30° C)

Answers / Notes

3.
Did ALL the salt dissolve?	epsom salt (7 g)	baking soda (1 g)
HOT water	yes	yes
COLD water	no	no

5. Solubility is affected by…

4a. Epsom salt is very soluble in hot water, but less soluble in cold water. Baking soda is moderately soluble in hot water, but less soluble in cold water.

4b. solubility of Epsom salt in hot water > 70 g solute/100 g H$_2$O
   solubility of Epsom salt in cold water < 70 g solute/100 g H$_2$O
   solubility of baking soda in hot water > 10 g solute/100 g H$_2$O
   solubility of baking soda in cold water < 10 g solute/100 g H$_2$O

The nature of the solute. Epsom salt was more soluble than baking powder.
The temperature of the solvent. Higher concentrations dissolved in hot water than dissolved in cold water.

Materials

☐ Epsom salt and baking soda.
☐ A gram balance and 10 mL graduate.
☐ A test tube with a capacity of 12 mL or more.
☐ A permanent marker.
☐ Hot and cold water. The stated amounts for each salt (7 g and 1 g) form saturated solutions at about 22°C. Consider "cold" water as something less than this (perhaps 15° C) and "hot" as something more (perhaps 30°C).

(TO) read and interpret a solubility graph. To predict the solubility of salts in water at specific temperatures.

SOLUBILITY CURVES ○   Solutions ( )

1. This graph shows how the solubilities of different salts in water change with temperature.
   a. List the solubility of copper sulfate at 0°, 20°, 40°, 60°, 80°, and 100° C.
   b. At what temperature do copper sulfate and table salt have the same solubility?
   c. Does temperature affect the solubility of all salts in the same way? Explain.

2. Find the solubility of Epsom salt and baking powder at 22° C. Relate your answer to the previous experiment.

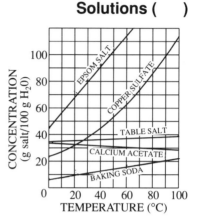

3. Measure out just enough copper sulfate into a test tube to form a saturated solution at room temperature (20° C). (You may need to apply gentle heat to speed the dissolving process.)
   a. How did you make this solution?
   b. Save half your solution in another test tube. Dilute the remainder by adding an equal portion of water. What is its new concentration?
   c. Examine both test tubes. How could you use them to visually estimate the concentration of an unknown copper sulfate solution?

26

Answers / Notes

1a. Solubility of copper sulfate in 100 g H_2O at various temperatures:
   0° = 23 g, 20° = 32 g, 40° = 45 g, 60° = 62 g, 80° = 85 g, 100° C = 114 g.

1b. Copper sulfate and table salt have equal solubility in water at 27° C.

1c. No. An increase in water temperature dramatically increases the solubilities of both Epsom salt and copper sulfate. Baking powder increases less dramatically and table salt only marginally. Calcium acetate actually becomes less soluble as the temperature increases.

2. At 22° C, 70 g of Epsom salt will dissolve in 100 g of water. Only 10 g of baking soda will dissolve at the same temperature. These concentrations were confirmed in the previous experiment in 1/10 the water: 7 g of Epsom salt and 1 g of baking soda did not dissolve in 10 mL of water that was cooler than 22° C, but did dissolve in water that was warmer than 22° C.

3a. The solubility graph indicates that 32 g of copper sulfate saturates 100 g of water at 20° C. Cutting back the solute and solvent to a tenth, 3.2 g of copper sulfate was weighed out on the gram balance and dissolved in a test tube filled with 10 g (10 mL) of water.

3b. The solution has half its former strength. It was diluted to 16 g solute/100 g H_2O.

3c. Compare the color intensity of the unknown solution with both test tubes of known concentration. If the unknown contains a darker blue than one tube but a lighter blue than the other, then its concentration would lie somewhere between 16 g solute/100 g H_2O and 32 g solute/100 g H2O. Otherwise it would be lighter than both (less than 16 g solute/100 g H_2O). *(Photometers are able to read the concentrations of colored solutions with accuracy by measuring the amount of transmitted light and comparing it to a previously calibrated standard.)*

Materials

☐ Copper sulfate.
☐ A gram balance.
☐ A 10 mL graduate
☐ Test tubes with a capacity of 12 mL or more.
☐ A candle, alcohol lamp or Bunsen burner, plus matches.

(TO) recognize that the solubility of some solutes in water decreases with increasing temperature.

NEGATIVE SOLUBILITY   Solutions (   )

1. Fill a test tube 1/3 full of calcium acetate. Just cover it with cold water, then shake vigorously at least 200 times.

2. Filter the solution into a clean *dry* tube. Does the filtrate contain any *un*dissolved salt? Explain.

3. *Predict* what happens as you gently heat this saturated solution over a flame. (Refer to the solubility table in the previous task card.)

 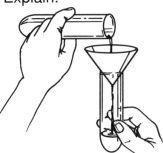 

4. Test your prediction. What did you observe?

5. Gently heat a test tube of fresh tap water.
   a. What happens to the air that is dissolved in the water?
   b. Both calcium acetate and air have *negative solubility* in water. What does this mean?

27

Answers / Notes

2. No. The filtrate is perfectly clear. All undissolved salt was trapped by the filter paper. (*Collecting this filtrate in a dry test tube keeps it from being diluted.*)

3. The graph line for calcium acetate slopes downward, indicating that the salt becomes less soluble with increasing temperature. As this solution is heated, therefore, dissolved salt should crystallize back out of solution.

   Glass is a very poor conductor of heat. By tipping the tube out of the rising stream of hot air directly over the flame, the top may be safely hand-held while the solution at the bottom is raised to a near-boiling temperature.

4. As the solution warms, a scum-like solid precipitates out of solution. It collects both at the bottom of the test tube and on the surface of the liquid.

5a. This air is forced out of solution, collecting on the sides of the test tube as the water is heated.

5b. Both calcium acetate and air become less soluble as the temperature of the solution increases. (*This counters the usual trend of increased solubility with temperature and is thus termed "negative solubility."*)

Extension

How will your heated calcium acetate solution change if you cool it back down in an ice bath or refrigerator? Try and see. (*The precipitate will redissolve into solution.*)

Materials

☐ Test tubes. Use a piece of paper towel taped to a straw to dry at least one test tube.
☐ Calcium acetate. Order this from a chemical supply company, or borrow some from a chemistry lab.
☐ Cold water. Use tap water in cold weather. Add a few chips of ice in hot weather.
☐ A candle, alcohol lamp or Bunsen burner, plus matches.

(TO) make a supersaturated solution of sodium thiosulfate that recrystallizes with the addition of a seed crystal to a more stable form. To observe that heat is released as the solution stabilizes.

SUPERSATURATION Solutions ( )

Sodium thiosulfate, also known as "hypo," is a hydrated salt. When you heat hypo it dissolves in its own water of hydration.

1. Gently heat a test tube that is half full of pure hypo until *all* remaining crystals dissolve. You can hand hold the test tube *if* you angle it over the flame and avoid boiling.

HEAT

2. Cool the test tube to room temperature (or below) under a gentle stream of cold water (or in an ice bath).
   a. Did the solution recrystallize?
   b. Does the test tube now feel perfectly cool?

COOL

3. Add one "seed" crystal of hypo to the cool, clear solution.
   a. Write your observations.
   b. Does the test tube still feel cool?

4. Most solutions recrystallize when they cool beyond their saturation point, but hypo *supersaturates,* remaining in solution.
   a. You know what "saturation" means. Define "supersaturation."
   b. Which form of hypo contains more energy, the supersaturated form or the recrystallized form? Explain.

28

Answers / Notes

2. If ice is easily available, use it. The colder you make the supersaturated solution, the more rapidly it will recrystallize once a seed crystal is introduced in step 3.

2a. No. The cooled hypo remains uncrystallized, dissolved in its own water of hydration.

2b. Yes. The test tube of hypo solution feels cool.

3a. The seed crystal of hypo immediately begins to grow and multiply into a network of beautiful crystals. This process continues until the solution completely solidifies.

3b. No. The test tube of recrystallized hypo now feels very warm, almost hot!

4a. Supersaturation means that the water is saturated beyond its normal capacity to hold dissolved salt, in this case hypo.

4b. Heat was given off as the supersaturated solution crystallized. Thus, the supersaturated form has higher energy.

Supersaturated Hypo ----➤ Crystallized Hypo + Energy

Materials

☐ Sodium thiosulfate. Find this in a photography store that sells developing chemicals. Don't confuse it with hypo clearing agent.
☐ A test tube.
☐ A candle, alcohol lamp or Bunsen burner, plus matches.
☐ Cold running tap water or a cold-water bath. Use ice if easily available.

REPRODUCIBLE
STUDENT
TASK CARDS

☞ As you duplicate and distribute these task cards, **please observe our copyright restrictions** at the front of this book. Our basic rule is: **One book, one teacher.**

☞ TOPS is a small, not-for-profit educational corporation, dedicated to making great science accessible to students everywhere. Our only income is from the sale of these inexpensive modules. If you would like to help spread the word that TOPS is tops, please request multiple copies of our **free TOPS Ideas catalog** to pass on to other educators or student teachers. These offer a variety of sample lessons, plus an order form for your colleagues to purchase their own TOPS modules. Thanks!

Task Cards Options

Here are 3 management options to consider before you photocopy:

1. Consumable Worksheets: Copy 1 complete set of task card pages. Cut out each card and fix it to a separate sheet of boldly lined paper. Duplicate a class set of each worksheet master you have made, 1 per student. Direct students to follow the task card instructions at the top of each page, then respond to questions in the lined space underneath.

2. Nonconsumable Reference Booklets: Copy and collate the 2-up task card pages in sequence. Make perhaps half as many sets as the students who will use them. Staple each set in the upper left corner, both front and back to prevent the outside pages from working loose. Tell students that these task card booklets are for reference only. They should use them as they would any textbook, responding to questions on their own papers, returning them unmarked and in good shape at the end of the module.

3. Nonconsumable Task Cards: Copy several sets of task card pages. Laminate them, if you wish, for extra durability, then cut out each card to display in your room. You might pin cards to bulletin boards; or punch out the holes and hang them from wall hooks (you can fashion hooks from paper clips and tape these to the wall); or fix cards to cereal boxes with paper fasteners, 4 to a box; or keep cards on designated reference tables. The important thing is to provide enough task card reference points about your classroom to avoid a jam of too many students at any one location. Two or 3 task card sets should accommodate everyone, since different students will use different cards at different times.

TWO KINDS OF FILTERS ⭘ Solutions (   )

1. Fold a soft absorbent paper towel into quarters. Trim the 4 loose edges into a quarter circle to make a cone-shaped filter.

2. Make a second filter like the first, from a "hard," unbleached, school-grade paper towel.

3. Mix a pinch of cornstarch in a small jar full of water. Filter part of this solution into 2 more jars, some through the soft filter and some through the hard filter.

FOLD AND TRIM

OPEN CONE

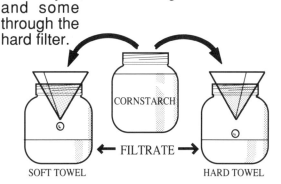

SOFT TOWEL   ← FILTRATE →   HARD TOWEL

4. Examine each *filtrate*. Are the cornstarch particles larger or smaller than the pores in each filter paper? Explain.

5. Add a drop of iodine to each filtrate. If cornstarch is present it will turn blue-black. What can you conclude?

6. Pour all 3 solutions into 1 jar. Close with a lid that is labeled with your name.

1

TWO WAYS TO PURIFY ⭘ Solutions (   )

1. Get your black cornstarch solution from the previous activity. Be careful not to unsettle the solution inside.

2. Gently pour off the clear top *half* into a second jar. How has gravity helped purify this solution?

3. Filter the remaining bottom half into a third jar. Will just any kind of filter paper work? What special property must it have?

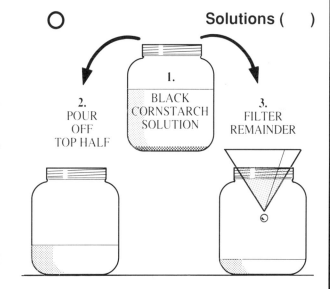

4. Cornstarch forms a *coarse suspension* in cold water.

    a. Name 2 ways to purify a coarse suspension.

    b. Explain how these 2 ways happen similarly in nature to clear up the water we drink.

2

A MATTER OF SIZE Solutions ( )

1. Boil water with just a *half* pinch of cornstarch in it.

2. Filter this into a small jar up to 1/3 full, using a hard paper towel. Fill a second *unfiltered* jar 2/3 full and seal it with a name-labeled lid.

3. Compare the filtered and unfiltered solutions. What can you conclude?

4. Did any starch particles, too small to see, sneak through the pores in the filter paper? Test with iodine on a microscope slide.

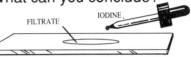

5. Add a pinch of sugar to a jar of water. Mix these combinations on a microscope slide with your pencil tip. Write your observations.

starch + iodine = ?
sugar + iodine = ?
saliva + starch + iodine = ?

6. Saliva contains an enzyme that breaks starch into sugar, helping you digest food. Was this enzyme active? Explain.

7. Seal the sugar-water with a name-labeled lid, along with the unfiltered starch.

3

DEFINITIONS Solutions ( )

1. Fill a jar with tap water and mix in a pinch of corn starch. Gently set your boiled starch and sugar solutions next to it, being careful not to slosh the water inside.

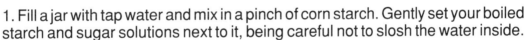

a. Fully describe the properties of this *coarse suspension*.

b. Fully describe the properties of this *colloidal dispersion*.

c. Fully describe the properties of this *true solution*.

2. When a *solute* (the smaller part, like sugar) disappears into a *solvent* (the larger part, usually water) and forms a clear liquid, it is said to *dissolve*.

a. Mix each combination and observe what happens.

b. Use the vocabulary above to report your findings.

SOLUTE (use 1/2 pinch)	SOLVENT (combine in test tube)
alum	water
non-dairy creamer	water
pepper	water

4

CLEARING MUDDY WATERS   Solutions (   )

1. Fill a small jar 1/4 full with soil. Fill to 7/8 full with water, then add just 1 drop of blue food coloring. Stir with your pencil.

I DROP FOOD COLOR

7/8 WATER

1/4 SOIL

2. Filter this solution into another jar through a hard paper towel. Continue until you collect at least 1/3 jar of filtrate.

FILTRATE

3. Soil contains a range of particle sizes:
   Sand — large enough to see individual grains.
   Silt — large enough to see with a magnifying glass.
   Clay — too small to see with a magnifying glass.

Identify and describe particles that…
   a. remain in the sediment of the original jar.
   b. were trapped by the filter paper.
   c. passed through the paper into the filtrate.

4. Seal your filtrate with a name-labeled lid and save for the next activity.

© 1990 by TOPS Learning Systems

5

COAGULATION   Solutions (   )

1. Add a pinch of alum to your jar of blue filtrate. Stir with your pencil.

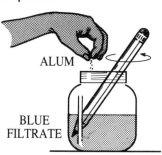

ALUM

BLUE FILTRATE

2. Filter half this water into a clean jar, then compare it to your original solution. Record your observations, then continue to filter the rest.

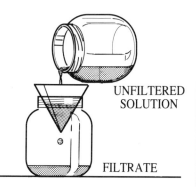

UNFILTERED SOLUTION

FILTRATE

3. Alum, an aluminum salt, *coagulates* (lumps together) a colloidal dispersion of clay into larger particles.

   a. How did this work to clear your solution?
   b. Seal your filtered water with a name-labeled lid and set aside for 24 hours. If coagulation continues, how might this solution look different tomorrow?

© 1990 by TOPS Learning Systems

6

PURIFY BY CHLORINATION ⬤ Solutions ( )

1. Gently pour off most of your blue liquid into a clean jar. Are any traces of sediment left behind in what remains? Evaluate your prediction from the previous experiment.

2. Examine the clear-blue liquid you poured off.
    a. Is this water free of suspended particles? How do you know?
    b. What dissolved substances does it contain for sure?
    c. What other dissolved substances might it contain?

3. Water treatment plants usually add chlorine to the public water supply to kill off harmful bacteria. Rinse your empty jar of sediment, then add just enough clear blue water to cover the bottom. Disinfect with a dropper full of chlorine bleach.

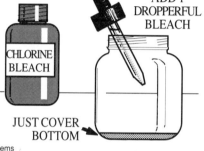
ADD 1 DROPPERFUL BLEACH
CHLORINE BLEACH
JUST COVER BOTTOM

    a. What changes can you notice?
    b. Does the water look clear? Is it fit to drink? Explain.
    c. When toxic waste is "thrown away", does it really "go away"?

4. Seal your remaining blue solution with a name-labeled lid and save.

7

PURIFY BY DISTILLATION ⬤ Solutions ( )

1. Trim a small paper cup about 2 cm high, to fit inside a small clean jar, resting on its side. Line the lid, plus about 1/4 of a side, with aluminum foil.

2. Fill the cup with just enough of your colored solution to cover the bottom. Seal it inside the jar, being careful not to spill. Set the jar foil-side down in a sunny window or outside in direct sunlight.

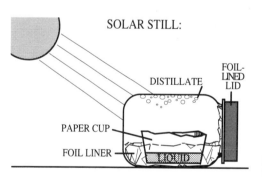
SOLAR STILL:
DISTILLATE
FOIL-LINED LID
PAPER CUP
FOIL LINER
LIQUID

3. Write about your solar still while you are waiting for it to purify your water.
    a. Will your *distillate* be free of dissolved food coloring? Explain.
    b. Draw a diagram explaining how your solar still works. Label your drawing with terms like *condensation* and *evaporation*.
    c. Compare purification by distillation with other water purification processes you have studied.

4. Explain how distillation happens naturally to purify the water we drink.

8

OIL AND WATER   O   Solutions ( )

1. Fill a test tube 1/2 full of water, then add a dropper full of clean mineral oil. Write your observations.

2. Even though air, glass, mineral oil and water are all transparent, you can still see the surface boundary of each material. This is because light refracts and reflects (bends and bounces) at each interface.

   a. Through what mediums do each of these light ray pass to the eye?

   b. Cap the test tube with your thumb and *gently* shake it. How is it possible to see oil bubbles in the water even though both mediums are transparent?

   c. Shake the tube vigorously. Why does the water look cloudy? Why does it clear up again?

3. Add 1 drop of detergent to your test tube and shake vigorously.

   a. Write your observations.

   b. Detergent *emulsifies* oil by surrounding the tiny drops so they can no longer grow back together. How do emulsions clean greasy (oily) dishes?

LIGHT RAYS

V.
W.
X.
Y.
Z.

GLASS
OIL
WATER
AIR

   9

IN BETWEEN   O   Solutions ( )

1. Fill a test tube 1/4 full with table salt, then 1/4 full of rice. Mark the volume with masking tape.

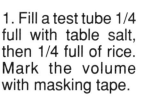

MASKING TAPE
RICE
SALT

2. Cap the tube with your thumb and shake vigorously. Do salt and rice keep the same volume when mixed together? Why?

3. Empty the tube and fill it to 1/6 full with salt. Gently fill the test tube with water, tilting it to retard mixing . . .

. . . continue filling until it brims over the top. Seal *tightly* with your thumb.

ADD WATER

1/6 SALT   DRIP DOWN SIDE

FILL BRIM FULL   CAP TIGHTLY WITH THUMB

   a. Turn the tube slowly up and down while noticing how the solution feels against your thumb. Write your observations.

   b. Explain why the pressure changes against your thumb. Use rice and salt as a model.

   10

ALCOHOL AND WATER O Solutions (   )

1. Fill a clean test tube 1/2 full with water. Hold it up to good light, then *gently* drip rubbing alcohol down the tilted side of the glass until it is almost full. Rest the test tube in a jar while you write your observations.

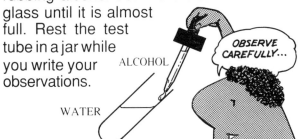

2. Hold the test tube with graph paper in the distant background. Do you see evidence of more than 1 phase (layer) in your test tube? Explain.

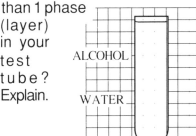

3. *Predict* how the solution will feel against your thumb as you tip the test tube up and down to mix the solution. Give reasons for your answer.

4. Test your prediction. Top off the tube with alcohol and cap it tightly shut with your thumb so no air is trapped.

5. Did the phases really mix together? How do you know?

TILT UP AND DOWN

© 1990 by TOPS Learning Systems   11

WHAT KIND OF MIXTURE? O Solutions (   )

1. Use the flow chart to decide if each solute forms a coarse suspension, colloidal dispersion or true solution in a test tube of water. Give reasons for each answer.

SOLUTE → Add small amt. to 1/2 test tube water; shake vigorously. → Solute gone? Solvent clear? — YES → TRUE SOLUTION

Clears? — YES → COARSE SUSPENSION

NO → Filter or allow to settle. → NO → COLLOIDAL DISPERSION

   a. A small pinch of powdered milk.
   b. A small pinch of baking soda.
   c. A small pinch of flour.
   d. A drop of India ink.
   e. A few crystals of copper sulfate. (Caution: copper sulfate is toxic. Keep it away from eyes and mouth. Wash hands after handling.)

2. One of these solutions can be purified by coagulating with vinegar. Experiment to find which one it is. Tell what you did.

© 1990 by TOPS Learning Systems   12

HOT AND COLD   Solutions (   )

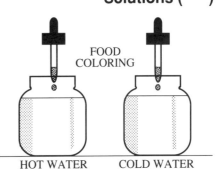

FOOD COLORING

HOT WATER   COLD WATER

1. Fill one jar with hot water; another with cold.

2. Wait one minute for the water to calm, then add just 1 drop of food coloring to each.
   a. Record your observations over the next few minutes. (Don't move the jars.)
   b. How does temperature seem to affect the rate of mixing?

3. Stir the warm solution (if it is not mixed already). Leave the cool solution alone.

   a. How is the hot *homogeneous* solution different than the cold *heterogeneous* one?
   b. Draw a dot sketch of each solution. Use more dots to indicate areas of high food-coloring concentration, fewer dots to show areas of lower concentration.
   c. True solutions are clear and homogeneous. Does food coloring form a true solution in water?

13

PARTICLE SIZE   Solutions (   )

1. Cut out a centimeter cube pattern. Fold and tape it together with small slices of clear tape.

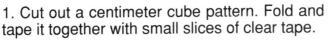

2. This whole "salt" cube measures 1 cm on a side. How many cubes would result if it were subdivided into…
   a. smaller cubes that measure .5 cm on a side?
   b. tiny cubes that measure .1 cm on a side?

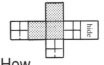 .5 cm
 .1 cm—

3. Remember that a cube has 6 sides. What is the total surface area of…   a. the single 1 cm cube?   b. the several .5 cm cubes?   c. the many .1 cm cubes?

4. Dissolving happens only at the surface of a crystal where water molecules directly contact the salt. When salt crystals are crushed into finer particles, how might this affect the rate of dissolving? Explain.

5. Test your hypothesis.
   a. Pour 1 mL of rock salt between scratch paper folded into quarters. Crush it with a small jar.
   b. Leave another 1 mL portion of rock salt uncrushed.
   c. Compare their dissolving times in test tubes half full of water. Did particle size make a difference?

1 mL CRUSHED SALT   1 mL ROCK SALT

WATER

14

SATURATION Solutions (   )

1. Fill a test tube 1/4 full with baking soda, then add water to 7/8 full. Cap with your thumb and shake vigorously at least 100 times.

2. Filter the baking soda water into another clean test tube. Did it form a…

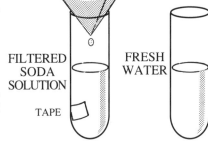

FILTERED SODA SOLUTION

FRESH WATER

TAPE

   a. coarse suspension? Explain.
   b. true solution? Explain.

3. Tag the test tube of filtered baking soda water with a piece of tape. Rinse the other test tube and fill with an equal amount of fresh water. Will a pinch of baking soda…
   a. dissolve in the filtered soda solution? Write your observations.
   b. dissolve in the fresh water? Write your observations.

4. The baking soda water is *saturated,* while the original pure water is now *unsaturated*. What do these terms mean?

5. Add 1 drop of food coloring to each tube. Don't stir.
   a. Draw how the drop interacts with each solution.
   b. Why does the food coloring sink in one liquid but float in the other?

15

CAN MORE DISSOLVE? Solutions (   )

1. Fill a test tube 1/4 full of rock salt, then add water to 7/8 full. Shake vigorously at least 100 times to saturate the solution.

2. Use this salt solution plus fresh water to do each experiment. Predict what you think will happen first, before you try it.

a. Add quarter pieces of seltzer tablets to each test tube.	b. Add a pinch of baking soda to each test tube.	c. Pool a dropperful of each liquid on inverted jars. Rest sugar cubes in each puddle.

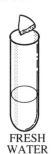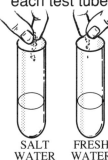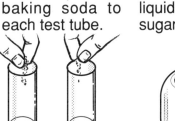

SALT WATER   FRESH WATER   SALT WATER   FRESH WATER   SALT WATER   FRESH WATER

3. Evaluate your predictions.
4. In each case, explain why salt water has a different effect than fresh water?

16

FROSTED GLASS Solutions (   )

1. Fill a test tube 1/5 full with Epsom salt. Add water to *just* cover the salt, then shake vigorously 100 times.

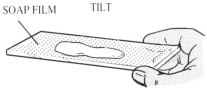
1/5 FULL

   a. Did you make a saturated solution? Explain.
   b. Comment on the solubility of Epsom salt in water.

2. Rub a drop of detergent over a clean, dry microscope slide. Wipe it off with tissue to leave a dry film.

SOAP FILM   TILT

3. Wet this slide with a few drops of your saturated solution, tipping it to spread the liquid. Hold the slide by its edge, so you don't touch the surface. Let any excess run onto the tissue.

4. Fan the slide with a piece of paper. When crystals start to form around the edges, hold the slide up to some good light and observe with a magnifying glass.

   a. Sketch the crystal patterns you observe.
   b. Identify the basic repeating unit in an Epsom salt crystal.
   c. Why doesn't this salt remain in solution? What makes it crystallize?

© 1990 by TOPS Learning Systems   17

BASIC SHAPES Solutions (   )

1. Rubber band 3 inverted jars together. Label with these 3 salts:

2. Make saturated solutions of each salt.

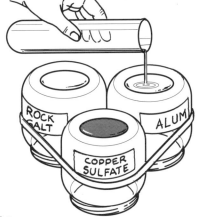

   a. Fill a test tube to 1/5 full with a salt, then add warm water to 2/5 full.
   b. Shake vigorously at least 100 times.
   c. Allow excess salt to settle, then pour off a *clear* puddle of the saturated solution onto the bottom of each labeled jar.
   (CAUTION: Copper sulfate is toxic. Keep away from eyes and mouth. Wash hands after use.)

ROCK SALT   ALUM   COPPER SULFATE

3. Set the liquids aside to evaporate overnight.

   a. Sketch the crystals that have formed on each jar.
   b. Identify the most basic repeating crystal shape for each salt.
   c. If crystals contain the same basic shape why don't the larger ones all look the same?

© 1990 by TOPS Learning Systems   18

WATER SPOTS **Solutions (   )**

1. Examine a jar of fresh tap water. Just by looking at the water, can you tell if it is really pure?

2. Place a drop of tap water on a perfectly clean microscope slide. Evaporate the water to dryness in a breeze or near a heat source. Then hold it up to some good light.

TAP WATER

   a. What can you observe?
   b. Could tap water be called a true solution? Why?

3. Repeat the analysis with water from other sources: bottled spring water, river water, aquarium water, distilled water, etc. Report your findings.

19

EQUILIBRIUM **Solutions (   )**

1. Trace the mouth of a jar on an index card, then cut out the circle. Punch 4 holes near the edge like this:

2. Add just enough rice to cover the bottom of a jar. Invert a second jar over the first, sandwiching the punched circle between. Seal the rims together with masking tape.

TAPE

RICE

3. Cut out an "equilibrium strip" and tape it like this:

4. Shake all rice grains to the left, then hold the jars sideways. Shake the jars vigorously 10 times and look; shake 10 more times and look.... Repeat until you no longer see any change:

EQUILIBRIUM STRIP

   a. This models what happens when you dump excess rock salt into a glass of water and half of it dissolves. Explain.
   b. *Equilibrium* means "change forward = change back." Does your model suggest that salt and water reach equilibrium right away?
   c. At equilibrium, excess salt in water appears *static* (there are no visible changes). Does your model suggest that this true for each *atom* of salt?

20

RATE OF DISSOLVING (1)　○　Solutions (　　)

1. Gently tap down 5 mL of rock salt in a *dry* 10 mL graduate. Pour it all onto a creased piece of paper.

2. Rinse the graduate and fill it with exactly 10 g of fresh water. How do you know you measured out 10 g?

3. Start timing on a clock or stop watch as you pour all the salt back into the 10 mL graduate of water.

4. Seal the graduate with your thumb and *slowly* tilt it up and down, stopping to record the new salt level (in column 2 of the table) after each half-minute interval. Always tap the side of the graduate to level and settle the salt inside.

5. Calculate in column 3 the amount of salt dissolved after each time interval.

6. Graph time (col. 1) vs. the amount dissolved (col. 3). Interpret your graph line.

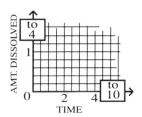

time (min)	salt level (mL)	amount dissolved (mL salt/10 g H_2O)
0	5.0	0
1/2		
1		
1 1/2		
2		
3		
4		
6		
10		

21

RATE OF DISSOLVING (2)　○　Solutions (　　)

1. Gently tap down 10 mL of rock salt in a dry graduate.
   a. Find the mass of this salt on a centered balance.
   b. Calculate the mass of 1 mL of rock salt.

2. Suppose 1 mL of rock salt dissolves in 10 g of water. Express the *concentration* of this solution in…
   a. mL solute/10 g H_2O?　　b. g solute/10 g H_2O?　　c. g solute/100 g H_2O?

3. Use your data from before to complete column 2. Convert to standard units of concentration (g solute/100 g H_2O) in column 3. Plot column 1 vs. 3 on another graph.

4. Salt forms a saturated solution in water at 36 g/100 g H_2O.

   a. Represent this with a dashed horizontal line on your graph.
   b. Did your rock salt solution reach saturation? Interpret your graph.

time (min)	amount dissolved (mL salt/10 g H_2O)	amount dissolved (g salt/100 g H_2O)
0	0	0
1/2		
1		
1 1/2		
2		
3		
4		
6		
10		

22

WATER OF HYDRATION (1)   Solutions (   )

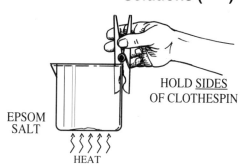

1. SLOWLY heat a SMALL pinch of Epsom salt in a small Pyrex beaker. (CAUTION: the beaker gets very hot even though it looks cool. Think before you touch!)

    a. Write your observations.

    b. Hydrates contain water as part of their crystal structure. Is Epsom salt a hydrate?

2. Clean the beaker, then test a few crystals of copper sulfate for water of hydration. Write your observations and conclusions. (CAUTION: Heat slowly, as before. Copper sulfate is toxic. Keep it away from your eyes and mouth. Wash your hands after handling.)

3. Repeat this test for rock salt and report your results.

4. Salts with water of hydration driven away are called anhydrous.

    a. Would anhydrous copper sulfate make a good moisture indicator? Why?

    b. Test your hypothesis.

23

WATER OF HYDRATION (2)   Solutions (   )

1. Weigh out exactly 1 gram of Epsom salt and pour it into a small, clean, Pyrex beaker. Heat thoroughly to drive off the water of hydration.

    a. Allow the beaker to cool *before* you touch the glass! Pour the salt back onto your balance and find its mass again.

    b. Express its loss in mass as a percentage.

$$\% \text{ mass loss} = \frac{\text{original mass - final mass}}{\text{original mass}} \times 100$$

2. Epsom salt loses water at 2 different temperatures:

$$MgSO_4 \cdot 7H_2O \xrightarrow{150°C} MgSO_4 \cdot 1H2O \xrightarrow{200°C} MgSO_4$$

    a. Compute its gram formula weight at each temperature.
        (Mg = 24.3 g, S = 32.1 g, O = 16.0 g, H = 1.0 g)

    b. What percentage of mass loss should you observe at each temperature?

3. Compare your experimental and theoretical calculations.

4. Do you think your anhydrous (or partially anhydrous) Epsom salt will gain weight during the next 24 hours? Test your prediction.

24

SOLUBILITY VARIABLES   Solutions (   )

1. Divide notebook paper into quarters. Fold and label each one as shown. Measure out these masses of salt on a centered balance.

3. Add hot water or cold water up to the 10 mL mark in this tube; dissolve in each portion of salt, shaking it vigorously 100 times. Record a "yes" or "no" in the table to indicate whether *all* the salt dissolves in each case.

4. Describe the solubility of each salt…
   a. In words.   b. In numbers.
   (Example: solubility of Epsom salt in hot water > 70 g solute/100 g H$_2$O)

2. Calibrate the 10 mL level in a test tube with water. Mark the bottom of the meniscus with a permanent marker.

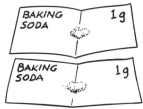

Did ALL the salt dissolve?	epsom salt (7 g)	baking soda (1 g)
HOT water		
COLD water		

5. Identify 2 variables that affect solubility.

25

SOLUBILITY CURVES   Solutions (   )

1. This graph shows how the solubilities of different salts in water change with temperature.
   a. List the solubility of copper sulfate at 0°, 20°, 40°, 60°, 80°, and 100° C.
   b. At what temperature do copper sulfate and table salt have the same solubility?
   c. Does temperature affect the solubility of all salts in the same way? Explain.

2. Find the solubility of Epsom salt and baking powder at 22° C. Relate your answer to the previous experiment.

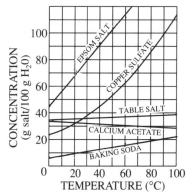

3. Measure out just enough copper sulfate into a test tube to form a saturated solution at room temperature (20° C). (You may need to apply gentle heat to speed the dissolving process.)
   a. How did you make this solution?
   b. Save half your solution in another test tube. Dilute the remainder by adding an equal portion of water. What is its new concentration?
   c. Examine both test tubes. How could you use them to visually estimate the concentration of an unknown copper sulfate solution?

26

NEGATIVE SOLUBILITY Solutions ( )

1. Fill a test tube 1/3 full of calcium acetate. Just cover it with cold water, then shake vigorously at least 200 times.

2. Filter the solution into a clean *dry* tube. Does the filtrate contain any *un*dissolved salt? Explain.

3. *Predict* what happens as you gently heat this saturated solution over a flame. (Refer to the solubility table in the previous task card.)

 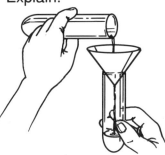 

4. Test your prediction. What did you observe?

5. Gently heat a test tube of fresh tap water.
   a. What happens to the air that is dissolved in the water?
   b. Both calcium acetate and air have *negative solubility* in water. What does this mean?

27

SUPERSATURATION Solutions ( )

Sodium thiosulfate, also known as "hypo," is a hydrated salt. When you heat hypo it dissolves in its own water of hydration.

1. Gently heat a test tube that is half full of pure hypo until *all* remaining crystals dissolve. You can hand hold the test tube *if* you angle it over the flame and avoid boiling.

HEAT

COOL

2. Cool the test tube to room temperature (or below) under a gentle stream of cold water (or in an ice bath).
   a. Did the solution recrystallize?
   b. Does the test tube now feel perfectly cool?

3. Add one "seed" crystal of hypo to the cool, clear solution.
   a. Write your observations.
   b. Does the test tube still feel cool?

4. Most solutions recrystallize when they cool beyond their saturation point, but hypo *supersaturates*, remaining in solution.
   a. You know what "saturation" means. Define "supersaturation."
   b. Which form of hypo contains more energy, the supersaturated form or the recrystallized form? Explain.

28

EQUILIBRIUM STRIP for activity 20

CRYSTALLIZED
SALT

DISSOLVED
SALT

hide

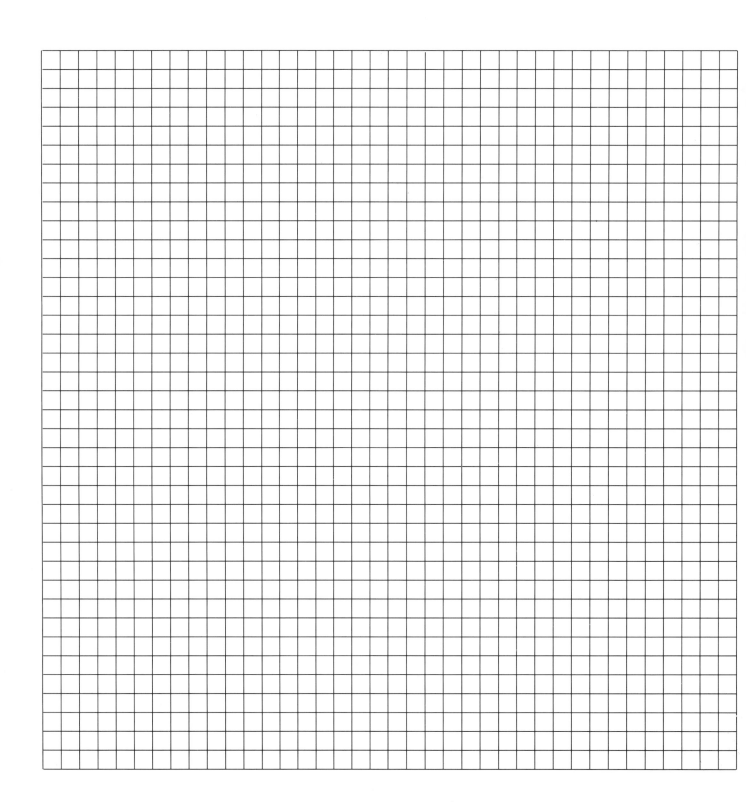